READING BY
LAMPLIGHT
A Scottish Bedside Book

READING
BY
LAMPLIGHT
A Scottish Bedside Book

Rhoda Spence

Stories of Edinburgh, Orkney
and places in between.

**THE
ORKNEY
PRESS**

Published by The Orkney Press Ltd.
12 Craigiefield Park, St. Ola,
Kirkwall, Orkney.

Published in 1991
ISBN 0 907618 27 8

Cover illustration by
David Grieve

Additional illustrations
by Rhoda Spence

Edited by Pam Beasant
Designed by Iain Ashman

Typeset by T & S Typesetting, Hewish, Avon.

Printed by Shetland Litho, Lerwick, Shetland

Gordon of Rothiemay's map of Old Edinburgh
reproduced by kind permission of Central Library, Edinburgh.

Dedication

*To Claire, who has helped me so much to bring
this book to publication. She was the baby who
was "hot to handle", (see "Helping mother nearly
eighty years ago"), and she still is, at times.*

Acknowledgements

These are difficult to make, for it is so long since I
wrote most of the contents of this book, that I cannot
remember in which newspapers they originally
appeared. But if copyright is claimed for any of them,
the publishers will be pleased to correspond with the
claimants and to make any arrangements which may
prove to be appropriate.

Contents

Orkney

Christmas

Memories

Weirdrie

Fife

The Passing Pageant

Verses

The Dream Castle

Introduction

When you climb into bed with your copy of *War and Peace*, you will find it a distinct relief to pick up this Bedside Book from the pillow. For you can open it at random (which is more than you can do with Tolstoy), and I hope that on any page you will find something to entertain, irritate, frighten or amuse you.

Would you like to hear about the goings-on in Old Edinburgh? Then turn to the Edinburgh section. Are you fond of poetry? There are verses at the end of the book. Do you experience a delicious thrill when the staircase outside your room creaks? Weirdrie is the very thing for you. But if you would prefer me to make you laugh, read *The Witch is Black Affrontit*. "I'll charm your willing ears. . . ."

R.S.

Spring Song

Winter, put up your sword!
Let hail cease fire.
We have the pledge of Spring
In silver script upon the sward
To make a garden where the Summer fell.
You triumphed then,
When he bled rose-leaves
On the withered grass
Torched by the aster,
Tolled for by the bell
Of the last lily in the fading ground.
Now the daffodil
Shows its bright trumpet
On each hill around.

Edinburgh

"The Guttit Haddie" – Gordon of Rothiemay's map of Old Edinburgh

Anyone who wants to wander through seventeenth-century Edinburgh has only to get a copy of Gordon of Rothiemay's map and look at it through a magnifying glass.

It is quite clear even without that — a wonderful picture of the "braw hie-heapit toun" as it was in 1647 — but it is fascinating to get a close-up of wynds, kirks, and markets, or to pinpoint some of the many buildings no longer there, like the great Nether bow Port which divided Edinburgh from Canongate.

Scots folk, with their talent for pithy nicknames, called the map "The Guttit Haddie", and in shape it is just like a haddock split open, but it is also a drawing of great charm, showing us a town that had made something unique out of its geographical situation, and was not without its share of trim garden plots. James Gordon, the parson of Rothiemay, in Banffshire, who left us this record of Auld Reekie, pleased the City Fathers so well that he was not only rewarded with the sum of 500 merks "to pay him for his pains and traveils in drawing of the said draughts," but was entertained to a collation and made a freeman of the burgh.

Some years later he was to give such satisfaction to the Town Council of Aberdeen for a similar map, that the members ordained the Dean of Guild "to buy or cause maik ane piece or silluer cup weightant tuentie vnce (ounce), and to buy ane silk hatt and delyver it to the said Mr James, with ane silk goun to his bed-fellow". It seems a generous recompense, but a little awkward if the artist had counted on paying bills with his fee!

That able draughtsman, James Gordon, first became

a map-maker to help his father, Robert Gordon, of
Straloch, who had been engaged to revise and complete
Timothy Pont's survey of Scotland. Pont was a
Caithness minister who set out to survey Scotland on
his own — a mammoth task considering the
rudimentary nature of its roads at that time. He
achieved a great deal, but after his death the maps and
notes he had left were in danger of being lost through
the negligence of his heirs, until James VI bought them.
Then Sir John Scot of Scotstarvet, Director of the
Chancellery, took the matter in hand, and approached
Gordon of Straloch to make the necessary corrections
and additions. It was obviously a task of national
moment, for Charles I wrote to Straloch urging him to
carry it on, while he in turn asked that his fifth son, the
parson of Rothiemay, should be given facilities to help

him. This meant that both men got Parliamentary exemption from certain obligations then placed upon the citizen.

Although their graceful and thorough technique suggests that Robert and James were working in an atmosphere of leisure, such was not the case. The setting to their efforts was the tremendous religious struggle between King and Covenant, and the elder Gordon was involved in support of his clan chief, the Marquis of Huntly. Straloch himself was beset also by the cares of an estate and a family of fifteen, and while James Gordon was pastor of a country parish, his post was not exactly a sinecure. He seems to have been plagued by a drunken dominie, who not only set a fearful example by dicing and drinking with visiting English soldiers "to the losse of all his money, nay his

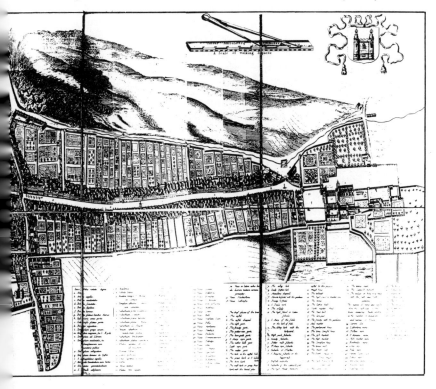

verie shirt," but made a scene in the manse during the minister's absence from home.

Another source of trouble was a stupid clerk, who got the kirk records into such a state that "a rapsody so confused never came out of any clerk's hand." Added to this was the necessity to reprimand parishioners who played football on "the Lord's daie" or offered up heathenish midsummer fires.

As if all this were not enough, he was more than once visited by the Church Commissioners, to find out why he was not disciplining his flock more firmly.

Under the circumstances it is surprising that the two men managed to put in 13 years of hard, concentrated work on the task they had undertaken. It has been estimated by Mr Caleb Cash, who has examined the maps over a long period, that among the collection now in the National Library of Scotland, 35 were by Timothy Pont and 64 were by the Gordons. Forty-six Scottish district maps from this source formed the fifth volume of Blaeu's splendid *Atlas of the World*, printed in Holland. Perhaps the most important contribution this brilliant father and son made in the great *Atlas* was the map of "modern" Scotland, showing the whole country in an outline so comparatively near to the one we know today that it is a striking tribute to their accuracy, and explains why Scottish cartographers relied on it for nearly a century.

But to most Edinburgh folk their greatest achievement will always be the "Guttit Haddie", that pawkily named rendering of the old town in its handsome heyday.

Magnificent sanctuary
that a Queen founded

During the fire one November in Jeffrey Street, how
many of the spectators realised that a relic of mediaeval
Edinburgh was threatened by destruction? Falling debris
menaced the ancient stonework of the rebuilt apse of a
Church nearly five centuries old. It is set sideways onto
the rear of the Holy Trinity and Moray-Knox Church,
and to enter it is to walk straight through into the past.

Like an outburst of triumphant organ music its
stone walls rise to tremendous height, merging in the
shadows far above into a vaulted roof of exquisite
simplicity. This is the ghost of the great Collegiate
Church of the Holy Trinity, a reconstructed fragment
of the splendid building founded by James II's Queen,
Mary of Gueldres.

Those who want to know how it looked in the days
of its prime must trace its history from here through
the libraries, art galleries, and museums of Edinburgh,
piecing together plan and altar-painting and stone
carving until they have a vision of the whole. Gordon of
Rothiemay's picture map of 1647 shows the church in
its original setting in what is now the Lower Calton,
but was then the suburb of St Ninian's just outwith St
Andrew's or Leith Wynd Port. Here the Queen had
already founded the Hospital of the Holy Trinity for the
maintenance of 13 poor bedesmen, when in 1460 she
decided to raise a magnificent collegiate church
dedicated also to "the praise and honour of the Holy
Trinity".

Encouraged, some say inspired by the King, she
received Papal blessing on the project, and among the
revenues bestowed on the new foundation were those
of the ancient hospice of Soutra. The building was to

consist of an apsidal choir with three bays, transepts with a central tower, and a nave. Close by was to be a chantry chapel, a muniment room, and collegiate building. To carry out the pious intentions of the foundress, the church was to be served by a provost, eight chaplains, and two boy clerks who were to pray for her soul and those of her husband and kinsfolk.

Had fate been propitious, there is no saying what architectural splendour the Church of the Holy Trinity might have attained. But from the first it suffered violent twists of circumstances which must have started almost from the moment its architect, one John Halkerston, set down his conception. In the August of 1460, Mary was widowed by the bursting of a cannon at the siege of Roxburgh Castle. Three years later she herself died, and although the edifice was even then distinguished by "magnificent and expensive work," it was not ready to serve for her funeral rites.

To her untimely passing may be attributed the unfinished state of what was to have been one of the most imposing collegiate churches in Scotland, the substitution of a tower by a gable, and the lack of the nave which would have balanced the height. Certainly it is not likely that these were errors of taste on the part of that artistic man James III, for from his reign comes the fine altar-piece painted for the church by a Flemish artist, and now on view in the National Gallery of Scotland.

This work, which consists of two panels painted on either side, is so vivid in execution that it opens a series of windows onto the fifteenth-century church and those who worshipped within it. For not only does the painter portray angels with gloriously tinted feather wings; he shows us real people — the kneeling figures of James III and his Queen, splendid in furred brocade, and Sir Edward Bonkyll, the first provost, a vigorous looking personality who must often have discussed building progress with the architect. Best of all, beyond these representations are inspired glimpses of the lofty interior of the kirk. The years to follow were stormy ones, but in the reigns of James IV and V, there are records of important new plenishings, an organ, bells great and small, rich hangings and silver vessels. Between 1525 and 1532 its provost, Sir John Dingwall, seems to have envisaged completion of the church, and not only paid personally for work on the fabric, but left a bequest for that purpose. Certainly its condition in that century must have been notable to merit the description of it in a Basle publication of 1550 as "a magnificent church called the Queen's College". Nearer our time experts extolled its Gothic splendour and the richness of its carvings. These live for us today in the spirited gargoyles on the exterior of the Jeffrey Street building, in a few pieces of finely wrought stone foliage in the annexe of the National Museum of Antiquities, and the fragment of a window tracery in Huntly House. As for the grinning monks and the grotesque demons or fabled beasts of an age which believed in the creatures of the Nethermost Pit, these are preserved for us in the drawings of that ardent antiquary Daniel Wilson, who set down everything he could before the church was demolished in 1848.

The Collegiate Church of the Holy Trinity, which had survived the storm of the Reformation and the despoiling of Cromwell's troops, fell victim last century to the indifference of the City Fathers, who sold the site to the railway.

Fortunately there were men alive then, mostly members of the Scottish Society of Antiquaries, who, finding their protests in vain, carried out all possible research, put the glories of the church on record and had the body of the foundress reinterred at Holyrood Abbey.

There was even a plan that the building would be rebuilt elsewhere, and its stones were numbered for that purpose, but during 30 years of debate they lay out on the Calton slopes. When the project came to be accomplished in the 1870's, there were only sufficient stones to erect at the back of the new Trinity Church that portion of the old choir cared for by its congregation today as a proud heritage.

Yet from its noble proportions, from the shadowy loveliness glimpsed in the altar-piece, from the grace of some fragmentary stone leaves, the imaginative can rebuild in the mind's eye a picture of the splendid church which once lay under the shadow of the Dow Craig.

The bairns of Auld Reekie

The bairns of Auld Reekie have no book devoted to
them in the wide literature on our fascinating town, but
how they peep through the cracks in stories about their
elders, particularly in the annals of eighteenth-century
Edinburgh.

It must have been a fairly confined life for them in
the closely-knit community that dwelt on the narrow
ridge between the Castle and Holyroodhouse.

Space was so limited that even in a well-to-do
lawyer's family the children had to be bedded down at
night on the floor of their father's room, while a
prosperous goldsmith's children were reared in a
nursery below the street level of his narrow booth
against the walls of St Giles.

Not surprisingly, the infants of this family died
young, all except the most delicate of them, who was
sent to the country for his health. It is probable that
wealthy folk with country houses as well as town
mansions would often leave their younger bairns where
they could have the freedom of large estates and ample
house-room.

Nevertheless there were plenty of small folk in
Auld Reekie to make the tall, dark houses ring with
their laughter and games, to run about the gardens that
sloped down on either side of the ridge or play in the
gutters of the crowded streets like the future Duchess
of Gordon, who was seen riding a sow which her sister
belaboured with a stick.

The general method of upbringing seems to have
been a mixture of sternness and spoiling, with more
indulgence than the following century was to show.

Perhaps because Auld Reekie was a cosy, intimate

sort of place the formality of the age was mingled there with a certain easiness and jollity of conduct, while in such crowded quarters it would be impossible to keep lively children under control all the time. Certainly it would be difficult to conceal tit-bits of news from the nursery people.

If they did not actually see history in the making, as they must often have done, they must have overheard whispered discussions in parlour and kitchen which provided topics for new games, and memories recalled with wonder in a later, more disciplined era. Was it gossip below-stairs in their mansion in Parliament Close that gave the Earl of Wemyss's children the idea of playing at Porteous Riots? Not unlikely, because their father's footman had been arrested as a ring-leader in that wild night's doings in September 1736.

At any rate the small girls of the family decided to re-enact the execution of Captain Porteous, and persuaded their brother Francis to take the part of the victim. With blithe disregard for the consequences, they hoisted the future fifth Earl up over a door, and did not see fit to cut him down until he was black in the face!

The Forty-five, with the stir of the tartan-clad Highland host occupying Edinburgh, left behind it one particularly engaging child's eye view of history, recounted afterwards by a very old lady, a Mrs Irving, living in Chessel's Court in the year 1829. She was only four when that romantic event took place, and, when out walking near Holyroodhouse with her nurse, was so intrigued by the dress of a Highlander standing in a doorway that she actually ventured closer to lift the edge of his kilt. In great alarm the nurse hurried to remove her, probably recalling fearsome tales circulated about the wild Highlanders, but the Jacobite gentleman merely patted the child on the head and "said something kind".

Even the dignified personalities of the Court of Session sometimes suffered the impact of Auld Reekie's small fry. Lord Coalstoun discovered this one morning when he leaned from the window of his house opposite

St Giles for a breath of air before setting out for
Parliament House in his full regalia of wig and gown.
Two young girls in the flat above were dangling their
kitten out of the window by a garter tied round its
middle, and inadvertently landed it on his Lordship's
wig.

In a panic they at once hoisted their pet, but by this
time it had taken a good grip, and the astonished
gentleman beheld his wig sailing aloft with no visible
means of support.

If the girls were often what the old people called
"sad romps", the boys were proper birkies. Bickering or
sporadic street fights between one faction and another
broke out almost twice a week even though they were
not countenanced by authority.

But what could the lumbering old soldiers of the
Town Guard do when both sides ganged up against
them at first sign of intervention? Sir Walter Scott
wrote with boyish glee of these "bickers" which are
mentioned in town records as early as the sixteenth
century.

"As well as these bickers, many individual pranks
come to light in books on Auld Reekie. Who but boys
would have thought of leading a coalman's horse up all
five flights of James's Court so that its astonished
master came out from the stair where he had been
delivering his load to see his beast staring down from
the top window of another house, neighing loudly to
attract his attention?"

That the famous men of Auld Reekie refreshed
themselves with childish company is evident. Allan
Ramsay the Elder, poet and song-collector, held
wonderful parties for bairns and young folk in his
house on Castlehill, and Mrs Murray of Henderland,
sister-in-law of his son, told how he used to make dolls
and dolls' beds for his young visitors. Then Charles
Kirkpatrick Sharpe, the antiquary, heard from his
mother stories of those who remembered the puppet-
stage and doll-actors which Allan contrived for the
amusement of young and old.

But the great event of the year, just as it is now, was the coming of the festive season, then concentrated on New Year. When the bairns got their handsel, they were drawn irresistibly to the Krames, those booths of huddled enchantment close up against St Giles.

What a pity some bygone artist has not depicted a shopping expedition of the kind. A sketch of the bright-eyed little creatures, gazing, fingering, choosing each bawbeeworth with loving and prolonged care, would make even more vivid the liveliness with which they scamper and giggle among the records of our braw "hie-heapit toun".

Mr Sheridan comes to town

On June 10 in the year 1761, Mr Thomas Sheridan, the famous Irish actor, arrived in Edinburgh. He had not come to give his well-known portrayals of Hamlet or Richard III, (although he was later "prevailed upon" to do them), but for a much more curious reason. He was there at the behest of the Select Society, to teach the Scots how to speak better English.

From a purely educational view-point this was not such a peculiar arrangement as it might seem, for Thomas Sheridan had made a speciality of spoken English and voice production, and had already lectured on these subjects in Oxford, Cambridge and Bath. But this was the touchy period following the political Union of 1707, and even to contemplate such a necessity must have rocked the older Scots to the very toes of their buckled shoes.

At this time the nation was obviously suffering from split personality. Certain intellectuals were drawing up lists of Scotticisms to be eschewed in prose-writing, others were making sure that their children would have the "elegant" accents of the Southron.

One who did both was James Beattie, Professor of Moral Philosophy at Aberdeen University, who wrote of his guidance to his son: "He was early warned against the use of Scotch words and other similar improprieties . . . his dislike of them was such that he soon learned to avoid them, and after he grew up, could never endure to read what was written in any of the vulgar dialects of Scotland."

On the other side of the fence were the sharp-spoken old ladies who were the glory of eighteenth-century Scotland, many of the witty legal fraternity and countless anonymous folk. One of the former, asked if a young acquaintance was Scots or English, replied caustically: "Ye a' speak sae genteel noo that I dinna ken wha's Scots!"

As for the great law lords, they seem mainly to have adhered to the auld tongue, and growled their judgements in its expressive idiom. Long after the Select Society had faded into obscurity, Lord Braxfield was to be heard complaining that anglified Francis Jeffrey had "tint his Scots accent and hadna' fund the English." "Whaur were ye educate, Maister Jawfry?" he asked him one day in court. "At Oxford, my lord," said the hapless advocate. "Ah, weel, I doot ye'll hae to gae back there, for we canna understan' ye here."

With the increased coming and going between the two countries a language problem had certainly arisen. The Scots spoke a tongue rather than a dialect, and one which had kept more closely to the mutual parent stem. It had its own distinctive idiom, and a vocabulary which had been enriched by contributions and borrowings from other lands, and while it might have been reasonably clear to the northern Englishmen, it distinctly baffled eighteenth-century London.

Comical misunderstandings were numerous, the most classic example occurring when the Lord Provost of Edinburgh and the magistrates were being cross-examined in the House of Lords about the circumstances of the Porteous Riots. The Duke of Newcastle inquired what kind of shot had been used to load the muskets of the Town Guard, who had fired into the mob on Porteous's order.

"Ou just sic as ane shoots deuks and sic-like fools wi'" said the poor Provost. Uproar followed at this apparent impertinence, and it was not until the Duke of Argyll, shaking with laughter, translated for the House, that order was restored.

Perhaps there was need for some liaison work, if only for the sake of our bewildered southern neighbours, and cultivated Thomas Sheridan, son of an intimate friend of Dean Swift, and life-long student of the English language, was the right person to effect it, even though he had a huge educational bee in his bonnet as to the moral potentialities of oratory and good English. His two courses of lectures were skilful, thorough, and a model of lucidity. In the first he covered the different phases of oratory and voice-production, and in the second "the whole state and constitution of the English tongue, so far as relates to sound."

Unerringly he put his finger on the main fault of the pronunciation north of the Border; the Scots laid their accent on the vowel instead of the consonant, so that they said "ba'ttle" instead of "bat'tle" and "ha'bit" instead of "hab'it". He recommended an hour's daily practice of reading aloud, slowly, and even speaking their thoughts aloud — a feat not without its perils if a Scots grannie or grandfather lurked in the background.

His hearers were impressed, and in due course the Select Society worked out an elaborate plan for prompting the reading and speaking of the English language in Scotland. Schools were to be opened in Edinburgh, manned by suitable teachers (one was actually engaged) and Mr Sheridan would not only help them to find the necessary staff, but would give advice and assistance as his engagements permitted.

Sixteen Ordinary Directors and ten Extra Directors — among them four earls — were elected, and funds were to be raised by approaching private persons as well as public bodies and societies in Scotland.

After the scheme was announced in the Press, in even more inflammatory terms, something went very much agley, and the Select Society lost support to such a degree that it seems to have folded up, at least for the time being. Perversely or not, many of the Scots folk wanted to keep their finely expressive speech, and did not relish the opportunity of being taught "to speak the English tongue with such purity as not easily to be distinguished from the most polite and best-educated natives of England".

Traffic problems in Old Edinburgh

The disgruntled motorist who rails at the present regulations which decree sternly where, and for how long, he may park his car, would probably be considerably surprised to learn that had he and his "bus" existed in eighteenth-century Edinburgh he would have had to submit to an almost equally stringent set of laws.

Although there was at that time no class of vehicles which exactly corresponded to the owner-driven motor, a Town Council Order, dated 1786, lays down very definite rules for the parking of carts and carriages, and the opening sentences of the document indicate that Old as well as New Edinburgh had its traffic problems. Space would indeed be precious in the old town with its buildings crowded together on the spine of the Castle Rock, (just as it still is today in the "City" quarters of London), and the Order in its eight clauses embraces carriers' and coal merchants' carts and brokers' and pedlars' stalls.

Complaints must have been lodged by the worthy burghers concerning street obstructions and insufficient traffic control, for the Order commences by saying that:- "Much inconvenience having arisen to the inhabitants both of Edinburgh and Canongate (note the distinction!) from Coal-carts, Carriers' Carts, and other Carriages standing upon the Streets, and also from late encroachments by Brokers', Pedlars' Stalls, and other incumbrances upon the High Street, the Lord Provost and Magistrates of Edinburgh and Canongate are determined, from and after Monday, the 25th of September 1786, to enforce the following Regulations in the strictest manner."

The regulation at present in force, which limits the
time a vehicle may stand in a busy street, is fore-
shadowed in the clause which states that all carriers
whose place of lodgings or upset lies within certain
bounds are to "unload immediately upon arrival, and to
remove their empty carts from the High Street until
they are ready to load for going away". Two hours was
the time allowed respectively for the operation of
arrival and unloading and reloading and departure.

The municipal authorities seem to have been
especially down on the coal-heaving fraternity, who
were severely enjoined not to let their carts "stand" for
sale upon the streets of the City of Edinburgh or
Canongate, "under penalty of having the coals seized
and confiscated". An eighteenth-century version of
"pass along please".

In the same strain, carters bringing coal for sale
were told exactly where to range their carts (on the
South Back of the Canongate, between the steps leading
to St John's Hill and the road leading to St Leonard's
Hill), and furthermore they were admonished:- "To
keep on the south side in a single row, and to preserve
the footpath clear for passengers"; or, in the same
orderly manner, they might vend their black diamonds
in the Lawnmarket. After reading this, one would not
be surprised to learn that they had a "white line" in the
South Back. Brokers and pedlars come in for a rap over
the knuckles in the same Order, and are warned against
exposing their goods for sale on the thronged
pavements. Only such stalls as the Magistrates had
appointed were allowed to be set up, and these dared
not encroach on the pavement, but were kept within
the strand or water-run.

What a picturesque glimpse of Old Edinburgh this
gives, with its street booths and semi-mediaeval
appearance! But one cannot help wondering what the
worthy city fathers of the City of Edinburgh and the
Burgh of the Canongate would have thought of a traffic
puzzle like the West End of Princes Street.

The Nelson Monument

To most Edinburgh people the Nelson Monument on
the Calton Hill is a pleasantly familiar landmark, first
pointed out to them as children when they stood in
Princes Street and watched the time-ball on its crown
drop at one p.m.

How many who look up can say that they have
been to the monument? A few perhaps, if only to take
their own bairns to see one of the most splendid
panoramic views in Edinburgh. There is more than this,
however, to the stone "spy-glass" which commemorates
the great little admiral, and which attracts thousands of
foreign and overseas visitors each year. If one lingers a
few minutes in the small museum at the entrance, the
pride and grief of a whole generation is made as vivid as
if the news of Trafalgar had just been announced.

What lies in the newspaper cuttings, letters, and
facsimile documents framed on the walls is not merely
the faded record of ancient history; it is rather
something written in the heart's blood of a nation. Even
the formal description of the battle in Admiral
Collingwood's dispatch — shown here in a
contemporary copy of the London *Times* — cannot
hide the admiral's profound sorrow at Nelson's death in
the hour of victory. As if he could contain his feelings
no longer he exclaims: "My heart is rent with the most
poignant grief for the death of a friend."

Nearby hangs evidence of an even closer personal
loss, the stricken words scrawled by Lady Hamilton on
Nelson's last letter to her. This begins tenderly: "My
dearest beloved Emma, the dear friend of my bosom,"
and at the end she has recorded her utter desolation in
broken writing which tells its own tale. "O miserable

and wretched Emma, O glorious and happy Nelson."

In his life of the victor of Trafalgar, Southey says: "The death of Nelson was felt . . . as something more than a public calamity; men started at the intelligence and turned pale, as if they had heard of the loss of a dear friend." It was during this great upsurge of national emotion that Edinburgh arranged for its memorial, and in 1807 the foundation stone was laid.

The cost, which eventually came to £1500, was to be defrayed by public subscription, and no doubt the will to give was there. But though Nelson's naval genius had saved Britain from the threat of invasion, the effects of war were still felt, and money was short. After work on the monument had progressed considerably, to the design of the architect, a Mr Robert Burn, it was discovered that funds on hand were not sufficient to carry it through. By the time operations were resumed years later, Mr Burn was dead and the architect in charge was a Mr Dickson, Deacon of the Trades of Calton. Under his direction it was finished, and opened in the year of another great victory, the Battle of Waterloo — in 1815.

As it neared completion there must have been great interest in the progress of the monument, which finally reached a height of 102 feet from base to crown. On the base, which is polygonal in shape, rises a slender round tower in four tiers which gives onto a look-out formed like a mediaeval bartizan. This is surmounted by a round cap-house crowned by another bartizan, and bearing the signal apparatus which has fascinated so many generations of Edinburgh children. Those who climb the 170 steps to reach a height of nearly 450 feet above sea-level are rewarded by a view which embraces towns, hills and river, and looks far across the surrounding countryside and coast. There is pleasant appropriateness about the fact that the memorial to a great seaman was later provided with the time ball which enabled shipmasters to set their chronometers at 1 p.m. Greenwich Mean Time.

Some writers say that the apartments in the base of

the monument were intended as quarters for old sailors, but this project does not seem to have come to anything. A restaurant for visitors was also suggested, and certainly a petty officer's wife who lived there for a time provided meals, sold strawberries and vegetables from the little garden, and catered for the dinners at Edinburgh's Nelson Club. But this was eventually discontinued and for long the quaint semi-circular rooms have made a unique dwelling for the keeper of the monument.

Most memorials attract criticism, and this one to Nelson has had its share of abuse, being likened to a "Dutchman's spy-glass" and a "butter-churn". Yet it has a simple dignity, and a purpose of use to seafarers that the great Admiral would have applauded. How his sculptured likeness, rising beyond a model of the Victor, dominates the little museum! And what a curiously modern look there is about the spare, alert face! That he had a message for future generations the citizens of Edinburgh realised when they expressed a hope that has been richly fulfilled in our time. For the inscription above the main doorway concludes by saying that the monument has been erected by them: "Not to express their unavailing sorrow for his death, nor yet to celebrate the matchless glories of his life, but by his noble example to teach their sons to emulate what they admire, and like him, when duty requires it, to die for their country."

Gaiety in the New Town: parties of the 1850's

With the exception of Miss Nicky Murray's austerely conducted dancing assemblies, Old Edinburgh seems to have bred a cosy social life. Aristocratic ladies often entertained their friends to tea in their bedrooms, with a plain-speaking old manservant handing round and keeping them right on points of genealogy, which were a favourite topic of discussion.

Well-bred folk of both sexes thought nothing of repairing to one of the town's oyster cellars for supper and dancing, and sometimes brought in the oyster-wives to join in the fun. One lady of high connections even went down the social scale when she became really desperate for a partner at cards. She would make a list of likely people, with the proper mode of asking them, and if those out of the top drawer were not available her maid was told to go to a humble acquaintance, called Lucky Spark, "and bid her come"!

But reminiscences of life in the Georgian New Town, particularly during late Victorian days, have sometimes given the impression that the flitting from the cramped lands of Auld Reekie to the elegant terraces and crescents of the New Town led to a grander and more formal way of life. Yet there was a link between the two, and for a long time a great deal of the old jollity survived in the social doings of Edinburgh society.

Nowhere is there a better or more complete picture of domestic enjoyment in the fifties of last century than in "The Story of a Lifetime", published in 1908. This book contains the reminiscences of Lady Priestley, one of Robert Chambers' accomplished daughters, who obviously inherited her father's delightful ease of style.

Though a native of Peebles, Robert Chambers became a noted figure in the Scottish Capital with his first book, *Traditions of Edinburgh,* in which he saved for future generations a wealth of Old Edinburgh history and lore, not to mention a host of lively anecdotes about its personalities. Men like Sir Walter Scott and Charles Kilpatrick Sharpe were astonished to find that this was the work of a youth barely 20. By the time Robert married at the age of 25, he was a general favourite and one of a brilliant intellectual circle.

He was fortunate in wedding a lady of great charm, with outstanding musical ability, and this, coupled with his own natural sweetness and keen intellect, made for a home life in which gaiety and intellectual pursuits were nicely mingled.

By the 1850's, he and his growing family were settled in Doune Terrace, where they made their own fun in the evenings, either with music and dancing in the front drawing-room or with paper-games in the back room. Some splendid results were obtained with the latter, for not only had several members of the Chambers family a marked facility for drawing, but they numbered among their friends such artists as Noel Paton, afterwards Queen's Limner for Scotland, and Richard Doyle, famous as the designer of the front cover for *Punch.* Noel Paton made some graceful and amusing drawings of family activities, while "Dicky" Doyle excelled at the game known as the five dots, in which pictures had to be constructed from dots drawn at random. In such hands, needless to say, the results were masterly.

As for the musical contributions, these sometimes included a delightful act from the younger children of the Chambers family. On these occasions their mother would sit down at the piano and begin to play. When she made "a certain rolling sound in the base" it was the signal for the little ones to run in, and standing on one foot, raise the other like a row of ballet dancers.

Christopher North, the friend of Scott and Hogg, was among those who joined in the gaiety of such

evenings, taking his shoes off and dancing in his
stocking soles with characteristic energy. In quieter
moments Mrs Chambers, an outstanding musician, and
the friend of such great performers as Jenny Lind,
would sing Scots songs and other old ballads with
wonderful effect, accompanying herself either on a harp
or on the piano. The great men of the period seem to
have entered into the fun of the parties at home with
tremendous zest, particularly Sir J.Y. Simpson, of
chloroform fame, who liked entertaining and being
entertained by the Chambers family. When private
theatricals became popular in this lively circle he asked
for the tableaux they had arranged to be repeated at his
house. So "Blue Beard", grouped by Noel Paton, with
rhymed words written by William Edmonstone Ayton,
author of the *Lays of the Cavaliers*, was given again
at Professor Simpson's house in Queen Street. It was a
great success, with the beautiful Eliza, afterwards Lady
Priestley, wearing a magnificent Oriental costume her
mother had bought at a sale. Professor Ayton had not
troubled to learn the words he had written and upset
the heroine's gravity by ad-libbing:
  "Fatima, my love, you're looking thin,
  Methinks you have a dimple on your chin!"
  But the comic turn of the evening was a tableau of
"The Babes in the Wood", in which Professor Simpson
and Dr Lyon Playfair took the parts of the hapless
infants, tastefully dressed in white muslin tied up with
blue ribbons! Lady Priestley relates that they "sucked
oranges as they wandered aimlessly through the wood.
They did not say much but looked everything, and fairly
brought the house down."
  Great men from farther afield were equally
enchanted by the warm-heartedness and versatility of
the young Chamberses and their delightful parents.
Thackeray, De Quincey and Dickens were their friends,
particularly Dickens whose assistant editor in
Household Words, Harry Wills, was married to Robert
Chambers' talented sister Janet.
  It is not difficult to imagine how people who could

act, sing, draw, and write would appeal to the vivacious
"Boz" and Lady Priestley tells of a night of theatricals in
London at Tavistock House, when Dickens, her aunt
Janet, Mark Lemon, and others acted a play by Wilkie
Collins. Later at her sister Amelia's house she attended
a brilliant dinner party where the conversation was
kept sparkling by such men as Dickens, Wilkie
Collins, Holman Hunt, and Chorley, the editor of
the *Athenaeum*. After dinner there was music, and
Amelia, who had inherited her mother's gifts, sang so
divinely that Dickens went down on his knees to beg
for an encore.

There is no doubt that the Chambers household
was an ideal nursery for genius. Not only was their
father a man of outstanding ability; he was obviously
the kind of parent who can impart knowledge without
tears. Moreover, with one foot in Old Edinburgh and
one in the New, he could tell his children of history that
was hardly cold, of great writers he himself had known.
As for the ballad-singing, the drawing, the breakfast
conversations, and the nursery romps with famous
men and women, these were in themselves a liberal
education.

It is not surprising that from such a nucleus there
descended a bevy of brilliant people. Two of the
Chambers girls married two brothers Lehmann,
members of a gifted German family; Amelia became the
wife of Rudolph, a painter of great distinction, while
Nina married his brother Frederick. From the first of
these marriages came the singer and composer, Liza
Lehmann, whose settings of the *Rubaiat of Omar
Khayyam, In a Persian Garden,* have given delight to
several generations. From the second marriage came
Rudolph Chambers Lehmann, father of three well-
known figures in our time — Rosamond Lehmann, the
novelist; John Lehmann, editor, publisher and poet;
and Beatrix Lehmann, the actress.

A gypsy comes to town

He should have been sitting in a woodland clearing, or on the edge of a moor, with the wind from the heath blowing through his hair. Instead, the gypsy basket-maker from Skye had his bent back against a shop front in a busy Edinburgh street. In and out his nimble fingers wove the willow-wands he was fashioning into a cycle-basket, the brown Belgian willow showing dark against the paler English stems.

The true gypsy type is not common in Scotland today, but he was certainly of that ancient race, mentioned so far back as the reign of James IV, and possibly existing here before then. He was finely independent, proud to be able to earn a living by a craft that was also his father's, and he told me that with steady work he could make as many as 12 baskets a day, also turning out beautifully woven dolls' cradles and babies' rattles. In summer, he said, he walked the highways, sleeping out under a little tent, and the names of the coloured counties tumbled from his lips as he spoke in his soft voice of places he had touched in his wanderings.

What a romantic story is evoked by the slightest glimpse of a folk which, in its purest strain must always have seemed in Scotland like a flight of tropical birds in a pigeon loft, and whose colourful lives ran like a scarlet thread through countless edicts and Acts of Parliament! In their dark, hawk-like faces and keen eyes, in their lithe walk, lives evidence of a race apart, which, though nomadic, had its own nobility, handsomely dressed and mounted folk, who got the permission of Scottish kings to administer gypsy justice to their own people.

There are numerous instances of Royal and

aristocratic favour shown to the gypsies in Scotland.
Sometimes it was on account of their skill as dancers
and musicians, jugglers, and strolling players;
sometimes, perhaps, for their support as fighting men
in those struggles for power which took place
unceasingly among the Scottish nobles. Gypsy people
are known to have "dansit to the King at
Halyyrudhous" in the year 1543, while from the latter
part of the sixteenth century comes an account of how
a body of them came each year to Roslin, and were
given by the Sinclair family living quarters in two
towers known as Robin Hood and Little John. Here they
presented several plays during the months of May and
June, one of them probably the famous May-tide play of
Robin Hood.

But they had other skills as well as these, and, like
the cairds or tinkers, were metal workers, makers of
objects in horn, pottery and horse-dealers, with much
reputation too for the spaeing of omens and fortunes
Strangely enough, not all the Scottish gypsies had the
dark Romany cast of countenance and swarthy
colouring, and there are numerous accounts of whole
families styled gypsies who were fair in colouring, while
many are described as pale and cadaverous, with dingy
white or rusty hair. How much this was due to
intermarriage with ordinary folk, how much to
confusion in the popular mind with tinkers, seems
uncertain.

Time and again old Scotland tried to tame the
gypsies, to make them settle to their trades, apprentice
themselves to masters, and live all the year round under
a roof like other men. In a tinkers' row, though they
mated with Scots folk on occasion, they were not to be
tied or tethered. As well try to harness the wind or hold
the stars back in their courses.

Now the growth of modern ways is accomplishing
what the law-makers of bygone days could not do, and
the people of the roads are gradually being absorbed
into the population. Certainly, Scotland still has its
tinker encampments, but they are fewer, while the true

gypsy is a rare sight north of the Border. Yet here and there he may be found, walking the highway with the free gait of one whose roof is the sky, walking to a secret lilt of the old minstrelsy which once enchanted king and commoner alike.

Auld Embro' – midnight

Nou the night's far ben and the toun is mirk,
Kimmer to hattock and horse wi' me,
We twa are bidden for witch's wark,
Wi steeple-bannet and ebon sark,
To ride wi bogles and darg for the Deil,
And tryst wi him in the kirk-yaird reel!
Then haste ye, gossip, Sanct Geillis crown,
Hums like a peerie wi' midnicht's bell,
And far below in the sleepin toun,
I hear the cry of the Watch,
"All's well",
Puir donnert fule, did he keek at the lift,
His een wad stert frae his aiken heid,
'Twad gar him skelloch to wauk the deid,
To spy twa shaddaws that flauchter and shift,
As thrum, thrum, we carlins come,
Wi' a hey and a heuch frae the tapmaist lum,
And clicketty clack, back to back,
Loup and fling till our auld banes crack,
By baudrons, houlet, and hoodie-craw,
We'll fit it weel ere the day sall daw!

Robert Burns

Burns' great work
as restorer of Scottish song

E'en then, a wish (I mind its pow'r),
A wish that to my latest hour
Shall strongly heave my breast,
That I for poor auld Scotland's sake
Some usefu' plan or book could make,
Or sing a sang at least. (*Epistle to Mrs Scott*.)

On an April day in 1787, an Ayshire poet and an
Edinburgh engraver foregathered in Auld Reekie — a
modest encounter which was to have unforgettable
results for lovers of Scottsh songs.

Surely destiny took a hand in bringing the two
together, for if James Johnson, publisher of the *Scots
Musical Museum*, had searched the world over, he
could not have found a collaborator so uniquely gifted
for his purpose as Robert Burns.

By the time they met, Johnson was well advanced
with the first volume of his song collection, which was
designed to fill the need for a work that would be
complete and reasonably priced, and he had secured the
help of several distinguished men.

From a technical point of view he was well
equipped for the task, as he had already invented a
system of printing music from pewter, which helped to
cut publishing costs. Educationally, he was not so well
endowed, but he made up for it by his genuine devotion
to Scots traditional song.

Burns took to him at once, and wrote with
characteristic warmth: "I have met with few people
whose company and conversation gave me so much
pleasure, because I have met with few whose
sentiments are so congenial to my own."

Method, foresight, and industry are not the
qualities laymen usually associate with a poet, but they
are what Robert Burns brought to the restoration of
Scottish song. Long before he met James Johnson he
had prepared himself for the task, for in his early youth
he had begun to take a keen interest in folk-songs and
ballads, and to set down discoveries of his own.

He carefully studied the work of earlier collectors
— men like Herd, Oswald, and Alan Ramsay — who
had played a brave part in rescuing this priceless
heritage from oblivion; but with his intimate knowledge
of everyday life, and contacts that embraced both
scholars and humble folk, he knew how much more had
still to be gathered in.

Faced with a project so dear to his heart, he set to
work with immense energy assembling material for the
Scots Musical Museum. It was indeed fortunate that
he and the publisher were so congenial, otherwise
Johnson might have felt that he was being carried away
by an elemental force. No sooner had he received one
"cargo" of songs from the poet than another seemed to
be on its way, accompanied by a coaxing demand for
proofs — preferably by return of carrier!

With his superhuman vitality, Burns managed to get
the next volume ready in ten months. Under his
influence the whole scope of the production was
widened. Johnson and Stephen Clarke, the organist who
did the musical arrangements, had simply visualised a
collection of existing Scots songs; Burns went much
further. Not only did he gather known songs —
combining through other volumes, getting in touch
with poets and collectors, tirelessly editing and
comparing — he set out to capture the floating
thistledown of Scots song, those incomplete stanzas he
was to restore and develop as only a great poet could.

In addition to all this he decided to write lyrics for
Scots airs and dance tunes that either had none or were
linked to unworthy words.

He was acutely conscious of the unity that should
exist between words and music, and more than once

emphasises it when outlining his ideas on folk-songs. In his Common-Place Book he wrote: "These old Scottish airs are so nobly sentimental that when one would compose for them: to south the tune . . . over and over, is the readiest way to catch the inspiration." Elsewhere, he says: "Unless I am compleat master of a tune in my own singing I never can compose for it."

Help in achieving this desirable state was not far to seek, whether he found it at his own ingle, where Jean sang like a woodbird, in Edinburgh with the child Janet Cruickshank, who rehearsed words and music for him at her harpsichord, or in quiet Nithsdale, where he listened to the overpowering voice of Kirsty Flint, a mason's wife. Once he wrote of having "an able fiddler at work", while J. C. Dick, that expert on the poet's part in collecting Scots melodies, believes that he must have been able to set them down in some fashion, probably with the aid of his own violin.

From the sympathetic relationship between James Johnson and Robert Burns came such pearls of songs as *Oh My Love's Like a Red Red Rose, Auld Lang Syne, Ye Banks and Braes, Bonnie Wee Thing, Green Grow the Rashes O,* and *John Anderson, My Jo.*

Johnson was sufficiently unselfish to let the poet take over the editing of his darling project, and had the good sense to defer to his superior knowledge. Burns shouldered the major share of the work, quietly compensating for Johnson's lack of education and Stephen Clarke's indolences. All the while he was pouring out immortal poetry, which was also to run through a third and fourth volume of the *Scots Musical Museum,* and to appear in the fifth and sixth volumes after his pen had been stilled for ever.

Alas, the same state of affairs did not prevail when the Bard collaborated with George Thomson, who invited famous poets and musicians to assist him in the preparation of *Selected Scottish Airs.* Thomson's entire approach to folk-song was wrong, for his main idea was to make it fit for the drawing-room, and to this end everything had to be refined and often purged of good Scots words. It was astonishing that a volatile genius like Burns remained so patient and courteous when faced with such finicking nonsense; it was little short of miraculous that he could rise above its petty irritations to contribute unforgettable lyrics like *Scots Wha Hae, Last May a Braw Wooer,* and *O Saw You Bonnie Lesley.* Those who want to trace the details of Burns' immense labours in the field of Scottish song will find many in his vivid letters to Johnson, Thomson and other correspondents. They will discover also that he would accept no monetary recompense from either publishers.

"You may think my songs either above or below price," he wrote, "for they shall absolutely be one or the other; to talk of money, wages, fee, hire etc., would be downright Sodomy of the Soul." He was equally unworldly about taking credit for his compositions and although he was supposed to have some method of marking them, did not identify many now known to be his. Yet where he could trace the work of an old or anonymous poet, he was always eager to acknowledge it. As for his infinite skill in "mending" countless half-forgotten fragments, who shall ever estimate its true worth?

Perhaps the Bard's magnificent achievement is summed up best by one of his most sensitive biographers, who is also editor of the collected letters. Professor deLancey Ferguson says in one memorable phrase: "Scottish song as the world knows it today is the lengthened shadow of Robert Burns."

Burns portraits –
and what was thought of them

Countless tributes have been paid to "The Immortal Memory" of Robert Burns. How many of the people who raised their glass in the toast to Scotland's National Bard knew what he really looked like?

From eye-witness accounts, Robert Burns is described as tall, and not stoutly but strongly built, dark complexioned, with large, dark eyes which sparkled wonderfully as he spoke. Measurements taken from his skull show that he had a head of unusual length and volume, a fact noticeable in the two silhouettes, and in the Reid miniature which was the last likeness painted of him. Describing his mouth, his brother wrote: "The lips showed a separation outward. To make the poet mim-mou'd will not do." A visit to the National Portrait Gallery of Scotland, Queen Street, Edinburgh, will show how the various pictures of him measure up to these descriptions. To take the most famous first, that by Alexander Nasmyth, is to find that this painter has given the poet a high, round skull, a fresh complexion, and the conventional Cupid's bow mouth of the day. But an artist must not be expected to be photographic, and Nasmyth was regarded by those who knew Burns as having painted a good likeness, if not sufficiently strong. Sir Walter Scott summed it up by saying that it resembled Burns seen "in perspective".

There may have been several reasons for this. To begin with, Nasmyth was doubtful about undertaking the commission when he was first approached by Creech, (Burns' publisher), for a portrait to accompany the poems. He was primarily a landscape painter, and a wag once said of him that he only "took aff heids to mak' ends meet". But Creech pressed the matter, for there was no portrait painter of note in Edinburgh at the time. Poet and artist met at breakfast in the artist's home, so that Nasmyth might study his subject's appearance, and they spent the rest of the day in a pleasant country tour which included Roslin and Hawthornden.

Next day Nasmyth began work on the portrait which is small as such things go, ($15\frac{1}{2}$ by $12\frac{3}{8}$ inches,) but surely one of the best-known Scottish pictures in the world. From his own account of proceedings, it was never entirely finished, as he was so pleased with results at a certain stage that he left the portrait alone for fear of spoiling it. On the back it bears the artist's signed statement: "Painted from Mr Robert Burns by his friend Alexr. Nasmyth, Edinr., 1787."

The other Nasmyth portrait is a full-length of Burns, developed long after the poet's death from a sketch made during their country expedition. It was worked up for the edition of Lockhart's Life of Burns, and repeats the head of the original likeness. Nasmyth also made two copies of his first painting, one of them for George Thomson, the song-collector, the other known as the Auchendrane portrait. In these there is more than a hint of the "massiveness" he had missed in his first impression. The ridges above the eyes are heavier, and the hair is thickened at the back of the head, while the mouth is wider than in the original. It has been claimed that the Thomson portrait was retouched by Sir Henry Raeburn, but experts do not wholeheartedly agree with this, nor does it account for the fact that both portraits show these developments.

It seems more likely that Nasmyth deliberately improved on his first painting, particularly as Buego, who engraved the Nasmyth portrait for the poems, was working towards a more massive effect. Buego also had the benefit of personal sittings from Burns, and his engraving certainly shows a much more rugged personality. He renders faithfully the dark complexion and the rustic appearance. But somewhere in the process he has entirely lost the poetic fire of the genius, and the face he depicts is at once uninspired and uninspiring.

It fell to yet another artist to take Nasmyth's impression and translate it into a third portrait, which conveys both strength and spirituality. This was Skirving, a Midlothian man, who executed the beautiful chalk drawing founded on the Nasmyth portrait. It is not certain whether Skirving met Burns, but it is known that he knew the Burns family, and may have drawn on his own observations. There is a strong tradition that this was so, and the sensitive face he shows is much more like that of the silhouettes and the Reid miniature than is the very earthy rhymer of Buego's engraving.

Both the silhouettes have the air of liveliness that such small transient things often have. One is by Miers, executed in 1787, the other, attributed to Houghton, bears an inscription by Grace Burns Begg; "Burns as Grandmother remembered seeing him." They depict the noble head, the short, slightly tip-tilted nose, the mobile mouth, features also noticeable in the Reid miniature. The latter was painted six months before Burns' death, and he called it "far the best likeness of me ever taken". These three portraits in little are all undisputed. But there is another likeness of the poet on a larger scale, which was produced long after his death, and aroused varying comments from people who had known him.

This was the portrait by Patrick or Peter Taylor, an Edinburgh house decorator and coach painter. He showed Burns wearing a wide-brimmed hat, and his portrait was said not only to have been done from personal sittings, but to have been begun before Nasmyth's. This was on the testimony of Taylor's widow, for the painter was also dead in the 1820's, when his work was first shown to outsiders.

It is curious that people closely associated with Burns should have differed so much in their opinions. Nasmyth, who had studied his face professionally, thought the Taylor portrait a bad likeness. So did others who had known the poet. A Mr William Hall who had seen Burns at his uncle's house, and who wrote an account of the circumstances surrounding the painting, said he would never hang it up in his house as a portrait of Burns. Yet against this is to be set the enthusiasm of Clarinda. "In my opinion," she declared, "it is the most striking likeness of the poet I have ever seen"; while his brother Gilbert said; "It is particularly like Robert in the form and air; with regard to venial faults I care not."

Orkney

Hint of foreign parts in Kirkwall

If anyone mentions Kirkwall to me suddenly, I remember little things like a fuchsia hedge, a milk bottle with a deep head of cream, and a street name plucked from a Viking saga.

Memory, I feel, has not done so badly in hoarding glimpses of homely charm, generosity, and romance from the many aspects of Orkney's county town. Then it really bestirs itself to produce the moment of deepest enchantment. This was when the 'plane first sighted the islands, malachite and amber against the dark sea, and I looked down on the lands which came to Scotland in pledge for a Norwegian princess's dowry.

Comely is the best word to describe Kirkwall's main thoroughfare where I was set down from the airport bus. On the one hand stretches a flagged walk lined by shops and shaded by the famous Big Tree. On the other the road widens to reveal the splendid Cathedral of St Magnus, ember-red in the sunshine. Beyond that it narrows to a diminishing vista of gable ends and crow-steps in pleasantly weathered stone.

There is an intriguing hint of foreign parts, as if some old skipper had come home with tales of Bergen or Danzig, though it is more possibly a folk-memory of the days when Orkney, from being a stepping stone for Viking rule, became a dependency of Norway. Like many people from "the Sooth" I had not realised till I dipped into Orcadian history that the islands had been under Norway for so long. For centuries Norwegian "jarls" ruled over a population of mixed Pictish, Norse, and other stock, Norse was spoken, and "udal" land tenure introduced.

Earl Rognvald was one of those jarls, a brilliant

adventurous figure, who took his fleet to the very shores of the Holy Land, yet laid his bones in the great Cathedral of St Magnus which he had founded. He raised the cathedral in memory of his uncle, the good St Magnus, who had been treacherously murdered by his co-ruler Earl Haakon, and showed in his own life that a hero of saga could also be a wise and Christian ruler.

It is one of the most colourful strands in the fringe of British history, and no one who wants to understand Orkney's ghostly ties with Norway should fail to visit the twelfth-century cathedral, where saint and founder are enshrined in massive pillars that once flanked the high altar. At the same time they will see an interior of lofty beauty, matchless between Trondheim and Durham, the older part of which was probably by Durham's architect.

James III of Scotland became master of all this when Norway failed to redeem the islands, and he annexed them to the Scottish crown. It is a moot point whether the act was legal, but with that kind of tact in which the early Stuarts excelled, he recognised Kirkwall's importance by making it a Royal Burgh in 1486, and gave the cathedral into the keeping of the city fathers.

Not far from the cathedral are the graceful ruins of the Earl's Palace and the Bishop's Palace, which were at their full magnificence in the early seventeenth century. Modern Kirkwall has made a delightful bowling green on the lawn of the Earl's Palace while a golf course and tennis courts elsewhere in the town cater for the more energetic.

But on the whole, restfulness is the keynote in this friendly town. No one makes plans, and there is always time to wander down to the harbour, with its vista of masts and funnels, or to drop into a café for tea and home-made scones.

For journeys farther afield there are good bus tours, and Kirkwall is an ideal gateway for these, lying as it does on the isthmus between the east and west mainland, with Scapa Flow at its back door. On a day of

vast blue skies and lark song I walked to the great
anchorage which sheltered the British Fleet in two
world wars, and ended by a wide, lone strand where I
would not have been surprised to encounter one of the
seal-folk.

The feeling of being hand in hand with legend, of
reaching out to the ancient world, is one of Orkney's
most subtle lures, and nowhere is it stronger than in
the dark moorland landscape, with its standing-stones,
which leads to the archaeological wonders of Maeshowe
and Skara Brae.

It is a weird experience to go stoop-backed into the
ancient burial-mound and see the runes and drawings
scratched on its walls by Norsemen who took refuge
from winter there so long ago; and an engaging one to
visit the little Stone Age village, with its minute
domestic and communal arrangements. Romantically
speaking, one should approach the island in a boat with
a dragon prow, but these days being past, modern 'plane
and ferry services make pleasant alternatives.

Information about these and everything else one
needs to know about an Orkney holiday can be had
from the Tourist Office and a list of Kirkwall's hotels
and apartments in private houses, in all of which there
is a welcome and good food.

On the cutting down
of the Big Tree, Kirkwall

What will the aged Dryad do whose tree must go?
Is there a home for such as her? I do not know,
I think I see her poor old wrinkled face,
Gazing from side to side in every place,
Clutching so sadly at a faded gown — that once was green,
And now is torn and brown.
"No room, no room!" her skinny grand-trees scream,
Drawing some nourishment from every stream,
I hope that if she climbs the hill she'll find,
Some sturdy group to shield her from the wind,
"Come in dear great-grand-tree" they'll fondly call
So that's a happy ending after all!

Onset of Orcadian Spring

At this season a rearguard action between obdurate winter and invading spring is often waged under Orcadian skies.

There are times when enormous pillars of cloud command the northern horizon, like giant hour-glasses filled with storm, yet even then the sun's advance has made the southern prospect intensely blue, drawing a responsive glow from the kindly hued gables and crow-steps of Kirkwall.

On such days the town assumes that subtly foreign look which intrigues the visitor; a Van Gogh or a Utrillo could feel at home in the paved main street when buds glisten fatly against the garden walls, and pigeons preen themselves high in the branches of the Big Tree.

He would find a rich palette in the shapely drystane dykes behind which regiments of daffodils and troops of primulas and crocuses are thickly massed, and see the flush of summer already touching the hedges of flowering currant and the parterres of old Tankerness House.

Above the goblinesque huddle of streets beyond the cathedral a green bloom is on the spidery trees, and a vast colony of crows goes about its shaggy nests with a comic gabble of question and answer. If anyone has doubts about the return of spring, it is certainly not the birds, for on days when pedestrians scuttle for cover from the merciless wind and rain, the blackbirds by the Willow Burn might be fluting from some Illyrian grove.

In the surrounding countryside ranks of daffodils ambush the eye, planted on the outer edge of fields where lambs stare inquisitively at the passing car. The little secret byroads run between banks covered with

primroses that bivouac from their verges up to the
sheltering dykes of tiny moorland dwellings couched
solitary and low to the ground, and the air, pure and
cold, carries the bell-like note of the curlew.

If, at April's end and May's beginning, winter, with
its battalions of mist, has retaken the advance posts, the
brilliance of evening marks the steady triumph of
spring. Sometimes gloaming brings a mass of violet
cloud, splendid as a chariot or a galleon in full sail. On
other nights the wide horizon is still and tender, ribbed
with azure and rose and lit by the growing moon. The
great waters are still too, molten gold in a quiet green
land.

To the skull of Saint Magnus

O noble skull that held a noble brain
Matched by the soul of him who still could pray
For those who wept when forced to slay.
At least four souls went Heavenwards that day
Or had a place made ready for that solemn chime
When gentle Death
Points skywards
And the failing breath
Gives hope of peaceful immortality.

To a thief — who stole from St Magnus

Give back the hand that was not yours to take,
Who steals from Heaven may yet feel Heaven's wrath.
Swift as an eagle, from the sky it comes,
Bringing a searching terror in its wake.
Such awful fire may on his life befall
That never may he find cool shade at all,
It seeks the hand that was not his to take.

The Vision Splendid —
(St. Magnus Cathedral)

Did poets first behold this vision splendid?
Enchanters summon masons from afar?
No! It was Churchmen shaped these rainbow arches,
And wrought stone flowers and fruit
To please the wandering eye.
When after twenty troubled years had ended,
Orkney and Norway met to dedicate
This shrine to Saintly Magnus,
Did they kneel to hear a gentle voice declaring
"I am Here."

Christmas

The Flanders Babie

The bairn in the faded brocade gown pulled her creepie
stool to the window, and climbing upon it gazed
through a hole in the thick glass at the crowded
panorama of Auld Reekie.

From the cellar room where she stood, her red hair
was just above pavement level. But it was enough to
give her a glimpse of the throng by the Luckenbooths.

There the torches shone bright on all manner of
splendid things laid out for the Daft Days, and town
and country folk jostled each other good-naturedly as
they looked and wondered.

Five-year-old Grizel Durie, who had been born in a
great mansion gave not a docken for the poverty of her
present surroundings. But she wished with all her heart
that the poor widow with whom they lodged would
convoy her again to the huddle of booths and stalls in
the shadow of St Giles'.

They had gone there a few days bypast, and Grizel
still dreamed of the glories of gingerbread men, sugar
plums and jumping jacks. Best of all she remembered a
fine wooden doll with painted black hair and scarlet
cheeks.

Tugging at Mistress Baxter's skirts, she had pointed
to it. The good woman had only laughed and said: "Aye
bairn, that's a bonnie Flanders Babie but I doot your
mither has nae mair siller for gew-gaws than masel."

With the philosophy of a child who has learned to
do without, Grizel thought this was likely to be so, but
she wished her brother Jamie would come in so that she
could ask him. Above all, she wanted her mother, who
had gone to Leith early that morning hoping to find
their father on a ship from the Low Countries. Her

father. She screwed up her tiny face in an effort to remember him. He was so muckle that his head near touched the ceiling. He used to take her on his knee and tell her stories or play cock-horse.

Why had he not won home when the King had come into his own again? It was too much for a five-year-old brain to ponder, and she jumped up eagerly when she heard the door-latch click. A ten-year-old boy came in, panting a little, for he carried a great armful of twigs. And as she trotted towards him he waved a small branch in triumph.

"A fire, Grizzie. I have been to the King's Park gathering wood, and we can have a fire. It will heat some brose for us when Mother returns."

He knelt by the empty hearth, building the twigs into a pile, and his sister leaned against him for warmth and company. "Jamie, will father be coming home, too?"

The boy looked sombre. "I know not for sure Grizzie, but Mother had it from an old friend of my father's that a ship from Holland was due, and that some exiled gentlemen were known to be on board her."

"Why has our father not won home lang syne?" asked the bairn nuzzling her face into his shoulder. "Oh Jamie, I wish he would come, for Mother greets at night, and we are often cold and hungry."

Then a heart-warming idea came to her, and she skipped suddenly, her dolours forgotten, as is the way of bairnhood. "Think you he will bring us something for the Daft Days? I wad like fine to have a Flanders Babie."

"Oh, Grizzie, lass," her brother remonstrated. "If he brings himself alanerlie we must be thankful. Mother says that he has been delayed because he was sick of an old wound, and then had no siller left to pay his passage home. Now she has managed to send him enough to take ship, but it was almost the last we had." As he spoke, the door opened, and their mother came slowly down the few steps which led into their lodging. Her delicate face was lined white, and her dark eyes swollen with tears. Dejection was in every line of her body. Jamie ran towards her, and led her to a seat by the fire.

"My father . . . the ship?" He could hardly get the words out. His mother shook her head, as if she had scarcely strength to make the movement.

"He was not there," she whispered. "And none could give me tiding of him."

Compassionate beyond his years, the boy bustled round her, removing her shabby cloak and the sodden, worn shoes. Kneeling in front of her, he rubbed her slender feet, while Grizel climbed on to her mother's knee and stroked her face.

"What dear bairns I have," the poor lady murmured a little comforted, though her world lay in ruins. With an effort she rose and hung a pot on the swee above the fire. "We shall eat soon and then get bedded. That way we can keep warm and forget our sorrows for a while."

The cocks had just begun to crow next morning when Grizel stepped quietly over her mother's sleeping form and pattered to the window.

It had come to her mind that a terrible thing might befall. Suppose her father won home after all, and there was no one awake to greet him? Sturdily she mounted the creepie and stood guard at her favourite spyhole, looking and listening as the ancient street came to life.

Among first-comers was a fish-wife from Newhaven, her skirts kilted above her striped petticoats. "Caller herrin'," she cried, her voice rising high and musical in the frosty air.

Soon other voices joined the symphony with "fine siller sand" and "knives to grind". The rumble of the carts coming in from the country made a bass to their lighter notes.

There was a clash of laughter as the servant lasses from the grand dwellings above tripped downstairs to fetch water from the well. Now the sky began to brighten, and Grizel could see the outline of St Giles' grow more distinct.

The noise in the Royal Mile had swelled to a steady rumble when the watchful child heard the lighter clatter of a lone horseman. Out of the morning shadows he appeared at the gallop, both man and beast showing signs of long travel. As he drew outside Grizel saw his face and set up a great clamour.

"Mother, Jamie, there is a muckle red-headed man at the door, and I think it is my father." With all her puny strength she tugged at the latch till Jamie came to her aid.

As the little family came to life, the cavalier was seen framed in the doorway. Then he folded his wife in an embrace so close that it seemed they would never part again. They broke at last, and he bent to swing the small girl into his right arm, the while his other reached out to gather his son towards him.

"Grizzie, Jamie, my dawties, ye are indeed a sicht for sair een." He turned to his wife who stood faint with the joy of his coming. "My dearest love, I took ship from Holland a month bypast, leavin the vessel at Wapping, for I had a petition to set before the King.

"The villains who escheated my property in my absence and turned you out of doors are to be punished. This afternoon we take coach for our great house in Fife."

He became aware of a tickling sensation in his right ear, and turned to smile at his daughter. The two red heads were very near.

"What say you, bairn, you would like a Flanders Babie, if I have the siller? Why, we can buy a whole regiment of them if you are so minded."

"I wad be content with one, sir," said the thrifty child. "But perchance Jamie wad like a troop of ginger-bread men."

Ghost stories at Christmas

I am not sure who started the fashion for ghost stories at Christmas, but in bygone days no seasonal magazine was complete without one. Perhaps it was Charles Dickens with *A Christmas Carol*.

Maybe it was just that the chill of the supernatural enhanced the charms of a firelit room with everyone gathered round the hearth after a good supper.

In our house we were fortunate in having a literary father who not only knew all the best ghost stories, but also wrote and told them superbly. After we had got past the age of howling in the night, he was usually cajoled into telling some of our favourites, and with chairs drawn closer to the blaze, we would listen in delighted terror.

Sometimes we would clamour for one of his own tales, especially *Cock Lorel's Boat* which had an Edinburgh setting. This related how a traveller, lodging in the Old Town in the year 1829, woke through the night to find the room rising and falling like a ship in storm.

When he ran to the window to discover the cause, he saw, not the familiar rooftops and chimneys of the building opposite, but a waste of tumbling billows. Even when the wind dropped the scene was one of terrifying weirdrie:-

"A ghastly light, tenuous and unearthly was slowly spreading over a dim, gently lapping sea. In the far distance lay a range of hills forlorn, unspeakably solitary . . . Suddenly an uncanny music floated across the water from the shore, a melancholy piping and taboring with a lilt to it. . . The thin penetrating tang of it invaded the blood, caroused through it, rapt the heart and mind

away into another airt than everyday." At other times
we would beg him to tell us what a Scots bishop had
related to an elderly relative about a night he had spent
in Glamis Castle — not a restful night.

But we really preferred to hear of the bishop's
relative's own experience in a house, rented for the
summer months in Cramond. The handsome old lady,
who was deeply interested in the occult, declared that
she had wakened one morning to see a young man with
red hair seated in her bedroom "reading a yellow-
backed novel". She put her head under the clothes, and
when she looked again he had vanished. No doubt this
was received at the breakfast-table as routine stuff,
but the family must have been shaken to learn that
others had seen the same ghost previously, and that he
was said to have committed suicide in the house,
which had formerly been used as a printing establish-
ment.

But if the environs of Auld Reekie had their
spectral happenings, the "hie-heapit toun" yielded tales
vastly more eerie than anything the glossiest Christmas
magazine could show.

Some of these are preserved in a sinister little book,
entitled *Satan's Invisible World Discovered*, a collection made
by George Sinclair, a seventeenth-century professor of
Philosophy at Glasgow University.

The yellowed pages with their long-tailed s's give
an air of direct reporting to the stories it holds, many of
which were contemporary with Mr Sinclair. For
instance he quotes a lady of standing, still living in his
time, who had seen some very odd happenings at the
Bowhead just before Major Weir's confession of sorcery
was made.

But one of his choicest pieces or horror in the dark
wynds and closes of the Old Town, tells what happened
when Thomas Colthart and his wife moved into a house
in Mary King's Close.

To begin with their servant-lass was forewarned by
a friend: "If you live there you will have more company
than yourselves." But Thomas, a sensible and devout

man, and a law agent, did not take this seriously, and they moved in.

His wife was full of apprehension and with reason, for after they had settled down to relax on the Sunday following their entry, she saw the head of an old man hanging as if suspended in mid-air. She swooned and it vanished, only to reappear, along with other manifestations, among them a naked arm which approached Thomas as if trying to salute him.

As the hours wore on, they were so invaded by creatures from the unseen world that they were driven to kneel on the bed, praying and crying out for release from this terror. At last the air was rent with a terrible groan, the spectral animals, the queer shapeless things that had gambolled about the floor vanished, and the tormented household was silent.

Brought up in Edinburgh, not so very far from such a quarry of the supernatural, it is little wonder that Robert Louis Stevenson later wrote that masterpiece of the gruesome *Thrawn Janet*. He is in the vein from the very first paragraph:

"The Reverend Murdoch Soulis was long minister of the moorland parish of Balweary in the Vale of Dule . . . he dwelt in the last years of his life without relative or servant or any human company in the small lonely manse under the Hanging Shaw."

If anyone knows of a better beginning for a ghost story than that, let them produce it. Set in the early eighteenth century, the story tells how the Reverend Murdoch Soulis takes Janet, the old witch-wife with the twisted neck, to be his housekeeper, because she is persecuted by the village women.

In a spell of oppressive weather "lown and het and heartless," the minister sees a great black man hovering round the village, and judges him to be none other than the Devil.

That night the true nature of the being he is harbouring under his roof dawns on him, and he guesses why Satan has come to Balweary. Hearing a tumult in Janet's room he rushes there to find her dead

— hanging from a single nail by a single worsted thread.

Hastily the Reverend Murdoch locks her bedroom door and hurries downstairs and out of the manse, with a terrible consciousness that he is being followed. All too soon he hears footsteps on the stairs. There was thrawn Janet "wi' her grogram goun an' her black mutch, wi the head aye upon the shoulder, and the girn still upon the face o't."

Among the traditional, as opposed to the literary, ghosts of Scotland, perhaps the most famous is Pearlin Jean, so called because of the kind of lace adorning her gown. Charles Kirkpatrick Sharpe considered her the most remarkable ghost in Scotland, and she is all the more curious for having come here from France, by whatever means such shadowy creatures travel. He had heard of her at first-hand from his nurse Jenny Blackadder, who had been in service at Allanbank, the Perthshire mansion where Jean's unquiet spirit walked.

For long, those who dwelt there heard the rustling of a silk gown (as Jenny did), the tapping of high heels, and the opening and shutting of doors. As late as 1790, two ladies visiting there got no sleep because of something which walked their bedroom floor all through the night.

The cause of this disturbance was supposed to be a Frenchwoman, who, in the sixteen hundreds had taken the fancy of the young laird, Robert Stuart, then finishing the Grand Tour in Paris. He had grown tired of her, and being summoned home by his parents, was about to leave when Jean arrived and mounted the fore-wheel of the coach to plead with him. Curtly he gave orders to drive off, whereupon the unfortunate girl was thrown down and killed, the wheel passing over her head.

No doubt the callous lover thought to put the English Channel between him and his fatal affair, but it was not so simple. "In a dusky Autumnal evening, when Mr Stuart drove under the arched gateway of Allanbank, he perceived Pearlin Jean sitting on the top, her head and shoulders covered with blood."

The other classic literary Scottish ghost story is, of
course, Sir Walter Scott's *Wandering Willie's Tale* in
Redgauntlet. This story of the tenant who went to
Hell to collect a rent receipt from his old landlord, Sir
Robert Redgauntlet, is too well known to need re-telling
here, but there is one wonderful little paragraph in it
which is like an eerie landscape on its own. Wandering
Willie explains Steenie's reluctance to play a certain air
on the pipes for the entertainment of Sir Robert and
the assembly of dead men:

". . . this was a tune my gudesire learned from a
warlock, that heard it when they were worshipping
Satan at their meetings . . . now he grew cauld at the
very name of it."

Certainly there is no need to go south for a
Christmas ghost story; we have more than enough of
our own, not forgetting those by the late Algernon
Blackwood. But if a supernatural mixture is wanted
there is no tale more likely to reoccur at unwanted
moments than M. R. James' *Oh Whistle and I'll Come to you
My Lad*, from his peerless collection, *The Ghost Stories of an
Antiquary*.

It tells of the unwisdom of a prim University
Professor who was foolish enough to blow an antique
whistle found in the ruins of a seaside preceptory.
What "came" to him not only followed him along the
sands, but some nights later materialised in the clothes
of an empty bed opposite his own and it had "an
intensely horrible face". Enough to deter me, at least,
from spending a Christmas holiday in a twin bedded
hotel room!

Christmas Eve in the forest

When the bus conductor put Charity Walkenshaw down
at Hollybush Lane on a raw Christmas Eve, he saw only
a done old wife, who would be better in her bed. He did
not know that he had set down by the wayside a bundle
of frustrations and regrets collected over 60 years. She
stood there dithering slightly, an object of pity or
ridicule, depending on how one regarded the flotsam of
another generation.

The landscape stretched indistinct beyond her as
she leaned against the stile before walking to her
lodging, but she knew the look of the sour earth which
lay beneath the foggy fields, knew by heart the outline
of the grudging plantation that mimicked spring and
summer at the proper seasons, and was gainsaid by the
shale bing close by.

"Not even a white Christmas," she was saying to
herself in a kind of meagre passion, "yet they call it
Hollybush Lane."

All the Christmases of a cherished Victorian
childhood, reft from her by sudden orphaning, rose up
to mock this bleak travesty of the season on the edge of
an industrial town. Crisp, white snow, fir-trees
sparkling under the moon, firelit nurseries, holly
wreaths and the milky sheen of mistletoe; like a
mirage, they hovered over the grim reality, before
vanishing to leave it more desolate to the eye than ever.

The minutes passed, and still Charity felt too weary
and faint to make a move from where she rested
against the damp wood of the stile. Indeed there was
nothing to lure her back to a chilly lodging in a flimsily
built bungalow, an indifferent landlady, and a gasfire
for which she had not the necessary shilling. But stay

there all night she could not. Already her feet felt rooted to the ground with cold.

She gave one more resentful look at the name-plate on the entrance to the lane which disappeared into the haar like a sinister tunnel.

"Such a Christmassy name," she murmured fretfully, trying to stand upright.

"It's the way to Christmas!" said a brisk voice close to her ear.

From out of the mist a figure had emerged, that of a tall woman in a red cloak with a hood. One of those new, bright waterproofs, Charity surmised, though really rather gay for such an elderly person. Or was she elderly? From the shadow of the hood peered a triangular face with brilliant blue-green eyes, and the nutcracker nose and chin of the traditional fairy godmother. "Come home with me for a posset?" the newcomer was asking persuasively. "You look frozen nigh to death, my child." No one had called Miss Walkenshaw child for half a century, or more, and it pierced her numb misery like the glow from a fire. "Very kind of you," she mumbled, "very kind. I never touch anything usually, but a hot drink would be most welcome. I don't feel at all well."

The stranger took her arm and guided her down the grey infinity of Hollybush Lane.

"There's a posset warming by my hob with all the flavour of the forest," she chanted, "and a fine seasonable night to drink it in."

Seasonable? Why yes! Charity realised with some astonishment that they were treading on crisp snow, and that the mist had cleared from the loaning, as a curtain rises on a stage scene, revealing a glittering path in the moonlight.

It must have started to snow while she was in the bus, she supposed, or this outlying district had been visited by an earlier storm, for the snow was inches thick, and the evergreens which loomed ahead were hung with festoons of sparkling white. Perhaps that was why they seemed so much taller than usual, lofty

enough to look like the outposts of a real forest instead
of a shabby little plantation on the edge of mining
country.

"Be of good heart," said the old dame, "'tis scarce
half a league to my cottage — no distance when you
walk with me. There you will rest, eat and drink. Then
I will show you such Christmas fare as you have not
beheld these many years. Silver nutmegs, golden pears,
nuts which break open to show goblin treasures . . . you
shall see."

Distinctly eccentric but kind, Miss Walkenshaw
decided, and her language, though curious, was not
unfamiliar. She had read phrases like these somewhere,
long ago.

"I had no idea this piece of woodland was so large,"
she panted, trying to keep up with the long stride of
her new friend. "As big as the mind can make it," was
the strange reply.

"Don't you feel nervous," Charity ventured,
"living by yourself in these days?"

"These days are not my days," said the old dame
serenely, "and there are many in the forest who would
keep me from harm. See you now that far-off glow? It
comes from my cottage window. Some of my guests
have found journey's end there already. Let us hasten."

"But I can't break into your party like this,"
protested the conventional Miss Walkenshaw. "For one
thing you probably have no room for an extra guest.
For another, well, I'm hardly dressed for the occasion."

The reply came swift and friendly as a warm clasp
of the hand.

"There is always room by Mother Hollé's hearth for
the lonely, and the light of my fire turns all garments to
gold."

By now the forest had widened to a glade where lay
a thatched cottage, sharply etched in the brilliance of
moon and snow. Though the cold was like a sword-
blade, swallows darted to and fro under the eaves, and
squirrels perched on the pile of logs by the gable-end.
The ancient wooden door, green in the silver light, bore

a knocker in the shape of an owl's head, but Mother
Hollé had no need to rap, and merely pushed the door
wide. Inside the room sat a little maid, and beside her a
young man. He stirred a skillet by the glowing fire, and
from it rose the sweet savour of all the seasons — the
heart-stirring perfumes of spring blossoms, the rose-
scents of high summer, the quince and apple of autumn.

From the linen napkin on his knee the youth drew
forth a little cake which he broke into several pieces,
offering it first to Charity, and though he handed it to
Mother Hollé and to the maiden as well, it never
seemed to grow any less. "I took the small cake with my
mother's blessing," he said. "Taste it and be happy.
Drink of this," he spooned some of the posset into a
cup, "and warm your heart for I know that it is chilled."

The mistress of the house settled into her chair,
casting aside her cloak to reveal a russet gown of
antique cut.

"Eat and drink as the younger son bids you," she
commanded Miss Walkenshaw gently," for soon we shall
have visitors, and you must feel well to join in their merry-
making."

Then a glow ran through Charity's poor body such
as she had not known for many a year. The posset
warmed her veins like an elixir of life, the cake tasted of
honey from the hives of a moorland garden, of yellow
farm butter, and eggs new from the nest. Thinking of
the scant meal she had foregone by not going back to
her lodgings, she almost laughed out loud, except that
she was not that kind of person.

Lulled by the comfort she slipped into a pleasant
reverie. How ill she had felt when she got off the bus at
Hollybush Lane. Now she was rested and fed, warmed
and loved. Above all, she was loved by these strange
people. She read it in the kindly twinkle of Mother
Hollé's eye, in the thoughtful deeds of the younger son.
Whose younger son? She knew not. She only knew that
after the drab life which had so heart-breakingly
followed a bright childhood she was wanted and cared
for, if only during this one Christmas Eve.

Mother Hollé was now emptying her pockets heavy with gifts to hang on the already laden tree. Then there came from the forest outside a great beating noise as of many wings, whereupon the old dame hastened to the door and threw it open.

In the starry dusk the air seemed full of white pinions, as seven swans, each wearing a golden crown, came to rest in the snow. Beside them stood a slender maiden also wearing a circlet, and as she touched each bird it cast off its feather mantle and became a handsome young man. One by one the new arrivals entered the cottage.

Now indeed we shall be crowded, thought Charity Walkenshaw, but she was wrong, for the cottage seemed to hold all who came, without so much as straining a timber. How the assembled company laughed and played and sang as the night wore on.

Into their midst came a wandering minstrel who could charm all the music of the spheres from his harp. When he touched its strings one heard the wind and the stars chanting together, and when he played the old Christmas songs, it sounded as if the cherubim were carolling in the forest glade outside.

Sometimes the latch would lift to admit the creatures of wood and water and hillock, a dryad in her green gown, a water-nix with shells in her hair, a group of red-capped gnomes, shy and smiling. The small beasts of the forest came too, moles and squirrels and badgers and the tiny field-mice, crowding round the hearth as tamely as the domestic cat.

Once the visitors had given a greeting to the old lady they melted into the shadows, so that Charity was not sure if they existed or if she had only dreamed of their coming. By now she was long past reasoning out what she beheld, or trying to explain it to herself. She was aware only that she was surrounded by the people she had loved in the books of her faraway childhood. Nonetheless she began to think that she must not outstay her welcome.

"It is time I went," she declared, struggling

reluctantly to her feet, sad that she must leave the cottage and trudge through the snow to her bleak lodgings. "I am already very late," she faltered half-heartedly, "my landlady will worry about me."

"The light that you have left behind you," they said, "will prevent anybody from worrying about you. You are going to sleep now and awake in a splendid city, where there is happiness always."

Memories

Helping mother
nearly eighty years ago

I wonder how little girls help their mothers in this push-button age? As an only child for 11 years, I was thrown a lot on my mother's society, and as she was loving, pretty and fun to be with, I was always dying to help her.

Yet, now that I look back on the duties I enjoyed, I find that most of them relate to a very different domestic scene.

Just as the Edwardian period gave way to George V's reign, I learned to lay the table for lunch, and put myself in charge of the cruets, two silver-plated stands holding salt-cellar, pepper pot and mustard pot — the kind of thing now seen mostly in restaurants or boarding-houses.

Every day of the holidays I cleaned out and replaced the mustard and topped up the salt and pepper if necessary; then on Fridays I had a gala morning, taking the stand to pieces, cleaning it with plate powder, and removing the paper doily which went under the pots. When I had finished I sat back and looked at the result with the satisfaction of an artist.

When we had friends to tea I made the butter balls which went on the shell-shaped dishes, feeling quite professional as I nicked a bit off the half-pound block with one of the wooden butter hands, and turned it into a neat ball or oblong. This had its tricky moments if the weather was too hot or too cold, when even the bowl of water could not make the butter tractable, but, on the whole, it was an amusing job for a child.

Later on I had great ambitions about helping with the ironing, but this was only allowed under supervision, especially as my intentions were directed towards a king-sized iron which was regarded as a great labour saver. This was an enormous steel iron with a top which lifted up, revealing a hollow interior which was filled with red-hot charcoal.

Mother said it was too hot to handle, and as I now had a baby sister, I was asked to keep an eye on her while the grown-ups were busy. Baby, a stirring two-year-old, was just about as hot to handle, and her main wish was to get at the kitchen cupboard, where the charcoal fuel was kept in a packet. If I let up for a moment, she would dive in and emerge like a small sweep, wiping her hands impartially on her curls or on her white muslin pinafore. As well as baby, we had acquired a pretty, general servant who had been a laundry maid, and I got tremendous fun watching her as she goffered caps and apron edges now only seen in Dutch or Flemish portraits. By then I was nearly 14, and with my own outside interests growing, did less about the house, but as I grew taller and taller I came in useful when the lace curtains were washed and had to be stretched to shape before ironing.

They were, I suppose, washed many times a year, but I remember best doing it in the spring. We had a neat little garden with a beautiful cherry tree at the foot, and it was an almost dreamlike experience to stand in the gloaming listening to the blackbirds and admiring the great canopy of white blossom as I pulled the curtain in rhythm with my mother.

I now over-topped her, so we pulled from rather different angles, but what I had in height she made up for in expertise. After the lace edges were evened up, we folded the curtains, walking towards each other with arms outstretched like the culmination of some ritual dance.

When I look back on all this, I realise that I am writing of another world — cruets, fuel-heated irons, general servants, goffered caps, muslin pinafores, and lace curtains. Like most people, I now have a washing machine and an electric iron, and I should hate to see women go back to the old, hard ways of working. Yet these duties had a happy place in the pattern of a child's life, learned as they were with pride, and done with love.

The circus that took Edinburgh by storm

It's bound to happen. It always does. After the Christmas dinner the family will gather round the telly — and the older members will start to reminisce about the "good old days" when live entertainment really was something.

The teenagers will smile and not believe a word. What after all can compare with wide-screen films and TV spectaculars.

But whatever the youngsters may say about distance lending enchantment, there certainly seems to be a case for Cooke's Royal Circus, which held Edinburgh enthralled for many years. From the dazzling night in 1876, when it opened in Edinburgh's Grindlay Street, until the sad occasion when it closed in 1913, the circus was a much-loved part of the Scottish entertainment world.

One of the main attractions was the brilliance of the Cooke family's equestrian acts. These not only drew many spectators but also earned the admiration of other professional riders, who considered it an honour to perform in their circus.

When the family settled in Edinburgh they came fresh from great achievements in international as well as British circus rings. John Henry Cooke, the handsome "guv'nor" of the Royal Circus, was born in a circus — his grandfather's — then running in America. By the age of four, John Henry had made his first appearance in the ring and at five he was actually doing a turn astride two ponies.

By the time he was 18 he was billed as "The Champion Equestrian of the Universe".

No doubt, of course, this was only what his family

expected, for he came of a famous circus clan, whose members had intermarried with other circus families.

But it was John Henry who was one of the prime movers in presenting a resident circus in Scotland. He was assisted by his brother, Harry Welby Cooke, and their cousin, Alfred Eugene.

Harry specialised in juggling — on horseback, of course — and Alfred Eugene had already been immortalised in that lively song *The Daring Young Man on the Flying Trapeze.*

Under such auspices Cooke's New Royal Circus promised well, for not only were the three partners rich in experience, but a new generation of stars were in the offing — John Henry's daughters, Ernestine Rosa and Edina Marion, and his sons, Talbot William, Leon Douglas and Leicester Alfred.

In time, Leicester Alfred took his uncle's part in the celebrated backward juggling act, which Harry Welby and John Henry had originated, and which they offered anyone a thousand pounds to emulate.

In this astonishing feat the two men juggled plates and balls on sticks between them as they cantered round the ring.

The Cooke circus, in addition to its horseback turns, was the first to bring water spectacles to the ring. Audiences were fascinated by productions like "Siberia", which reproduced the conditions and hazards of a Russian Winter, and "The Scalp Hunters" which for good measure included a rousing fight between cowboys and Indians and the dynamiting of a dam.

In most of these aquatic spectacles things became a little damp and gritty for spectators in the front row of seats, but that was no doubt a small price to pay for so much excitement.

I saw Cooke's Circus 70-odd years ago when it was in its sunset days. The beloved Guv'nor must have been in his late seventies. But he and his circus still brought to the Christmas holidays that rich, end-of-an-era glamour that lingers in the memory like a shower of sequins.

The gate

I remember this gate so well,
It leads to the far meadow,
Our childhood kingdom of green and golden shadow.
We squeezed through the bars
To hear the grasshopper tirring,
Looking down for the skylark's nest,
And up to the hidden blackbird
Shouting and stirring
With the ardent song of summer
In its breast.
Were they at different times and seasons— I forget;
To me it was one long day, and I see it yet,
Sun-warmed and happier than recent years;
Now I lean my head on this gate
To endless June —
Too tall to enter in, too old for tears,
But child enough to hear a dead bird's tune.

Grasshopper summer

Every summer has its themesong, one year the
incessant patter of raindrops carried on too long for the
taste of the listeners; another, the soft "trr-trr" of the
grasshoppers, sounding rather like an elfin percussion
band practising in the undergrowth. I heard it first in
the drowsy warmth of a Gloucestershire garden as I lay
half asleep under the shade of an oak tree. On the
distant horizon Bredon Hill and the "coloured counties"
shimmered in the heat, and the great velvety bees,
zooming among the roses, provided a pleasant base to
the grasshopper's lighter notes. I was to hear the same
duet again three weeks later, and some hundreds of
miles farther north, on a hillside in Argyll, and
between these two insect concerts lay a whole world of
contrast. Yet some things these two regions have in
common. Both are outstandingly beautiful in their own
fashion, both lull the stranger into a kind of peaceful
half-dream, uncurling the nerves, slowing the
movements with their warm airs and the soft voices of
their folk. And both have their roots deep in the past,
down through the top soil of history and romance to
the ancient earth of legend. Motoring in a leisurely way
through the Gloucestershire country-side was like
turning page after page of an English story-book. For
here were the cottages of golden-hued stone and thatch,
the burgeoning gardens, the little tree-shadowed
churches which are the illustrator's delight. Here were
the quiet but prosperous market towns, their venerable
timbered buildings a little bowed with the weight of the
centuries, but exquisitely kept and cherished. And here
were the glorious abbeys, where the choir music rose
like a flight of silver birds to the carven roof and the

stone effigies of knights and bishops were dimly seen in the surrounding dusk.

From the roads that twined through the unspoiled villages of the Cotswolds, were glimpsed a score of enchanting vignettes. At one turn of the way it was a beautiful wrought gateway screening the frontage of a house that was young when Charles II sat on the Throne. Farther on it was a pleasant dwelling made from two old cottages. Inside its casement window hung a wicker cage with two pet doves, while down the hills to the meadows beyond sloped the garden, a vista so rich in colour that it resembled a picture in embroidery.

Utter peace was the keynote everywhere; cats drowsed on door-steps worn hollow with the tread of many generations; dappled boughs hung slumbrous over walls that seemed to have soaked in the sun of countless summers. It was, therefore, almost a physical shock to come to a signpost which bore the name of one of the most sanguinary battles in the Wars of the Roses, that mediæval struggle which once tore England apart. To go from Gloucestershire to Argyll was rather like turning from a delicate water-colour to the jewelled tones of an oil-painting. The train journey soon made it clear that colour and shape grow richer and more dramatic with the first sight of the Highland hills, and by the time the border into Argyll was crossed they had already "cuist the glamourie" on the beholder. Anything might happen in this land of legend, where the very beginnings of Scotland can be traced. A great golden cloud lay asleep in a corrie, Loch Awe came into view mirroring the ruined towers of Kilchurn Castle, which was built when its lord was at the crusades. Deidre's Loch Etive glittered like a sapphire in the evening sun, and as far as the eye could see the landscape rose and fell in unbelievable splendour.

Journey's end was a snug timber house set in a hillside garden on the outskirts of Oban, and here the grasshoppers continued the theme-song of the languorous weather, "trr-trr" in the long grass. It was too hot to leave the shade of the one tree, but in the cool of the evening there was a road to the hills which offered an enticing prospect as it went up and down, through sun and shadow, to the peaks now turning deepest purple.

As the road turned towards the higher hill-slopes scores of wild flowers caught the eye in the ditches, more than an unversed person like myself could ever name. Though the heather and the rowans were early bringing a deep autumnal note to the scene, the wildings still displayed summer's bounty in countless shapes and colours, making a way-side tapestry so rich that any botanist would turn hermit here for its sake.

After the first visit to Oban harbour it became obvious that the holiday would be one long struggle for choice between the hill road and the sea road. Or would it? Could there be many sights in this island so amazing as the sea prospect from Oban Bay with the green dragon shape of Kerrera cutting across the enamelled blue of the Sound, with the hint of the Western Isles beyond? Everything in the still air looked as if painted on the water; the tawny sails of fishing boats, the white hulls of the yachts, the darker massing of shapes near the harbour when the lobster boats come in.

This was the drop scene to the last act of the Grasshopper Summer; the kind of thing that nature does so much better than the most gifted scene painter.

Weirdrie

Inspiration of a famous horror novel

"We will all write a ghost story," said Lord Byron. Little did he know that his proposal was to inspire one of the most famous horror tales the world has ever known. Two of the characters in this exciting pact were dead before Queen Victoria came to the throne, yet the thrill of Mary Shelley's *Frankenstein* is renewed every time some cinema screens one of the films based on her idea.

The scene of the conversation was Geneva, in the year 1816. Nineteen-year-old Mary Godwin and Percy Bysshe Shelley, the poet who was afterwards to become her husband, had recently made Lord Byron's acquaintance, and on the evening in question were visiting him at the Villa Diodati. The weather had been wet and dismal, and the coterie of young intellectuals had amused themselves by reading a collection of ghost stories evidently of the most "Gothic" description.

Now, as they sat round a wood fire, along with John Polidori, Byron's doctor, the talk was all of ghosts and apparitions. The older poet heightened the tension by quoting a macabre passage from Coleridge's newly published poem *Christabel*, and Shelley, always highly strung, was reminded of a horrible legend, the thought of which sent him screaming from the room.

After Shelley had been quietened, Byron then made his suggestion, and in that super-charged atmosphere its execution must have seemed easy. But though all four started on the project, it was only the serene-looking girl who was to carry it to a successful conclusion. Even she found difficulty in beginning, and day after day had to confess that she had not thought of a suitable idea.

The spark to fire her imagination came one night

after she had listened while Byron and Shelley discussed the nature of the principle of life. The world of science was at that time rapidly expanding its boundaries. Dr Darwin had reported movement in a piece of vermicelli kept in a glass case, and such comparatively recent discoveries as galvanism had suggested that a corpse might be reanimated, or a creature be made from component parts and brought to life.

With these weird ideas in her mind Mary went late to bed and could not sleep. As she lay with closed eyes, a series of pictures came to her. She saw, in fancy, the hero she was afterwards to name Frankenstein — "pale student of unhallowed arts kneeling beside the thing he had put together."

She imagined the hideous being he had created, and his own terror as it began to move. She thought of him rushing away from his awful handiwork in the hope that it might not be strong enough to survive. Most dreadful vision of all — she conjured up his emotions as he woke from sleep to find the creature at his bedside "looking on him with yellow, watery, but speculative eyes." After this terrible night, Mary was able to tell the others next day that she at last had an idea. She began to write the tale which was to add a new word to the English language, setting down first the chilling phrase which now forms the opening of Chapter V: "It was on a dreary night of November."

For Scottish readers, there is particular interest in the fact that in the preface to *Frankenstein*, Mary attributes the awakening of her imagination to her stay in a house on the northern shore of the River Tay, near Dundee. She was only 15 when she lived there for a time with the Baxters — friends of her father, William Godwin. Here, for the first time in her life, she was really free, and as she dreamed away the hours under the trees, or roamed the bare hill-slopes, she began to weave stories, though the talent was to lie dormant until she met Shelley.

It is well over a century and a half since the famous book was first submitted to a publisher, and it was turned down by two different firms before it was accepted and published in March 1818. The reviews were a tribute to its sensational impact, but some of them condemned the "impiety" of the main idea, and all of them assumed that the writer was a man. Yet, while shocked by the terrifying conception of a man-made creature, the critics acknowledged the power and gripping quality of *Frankenstein*. When the author's identity became known, *Blackwood's Edinburgh Magazine* commented: "For a man, it was excellent, but for a woman it was wonderful." The writer might have added that for a 19-year-old girl, it was a unique triumph.

In due course, a plot so full of dramatic possibilities was translated to the stage, and the story of the unhappy monster, who wanted to be loved and inspired only terror, filled many a London theatre from the year 1832 onwards. Mary Shelley, by now a widow, was present at the earliest production in the English Opera House, and although she thought the story "not well managed," and was rather amused by the whole affair, she was impressed by the acting of Mr T. Cooke, who played the monster. This actor was to remain the finest exponent of the part, in which he wore a make-up evidently quite as fearsome as Boris Karloff's in the film.

During the years that followed, countless dramatic versions were written, some serious, others in burlesque form, and great liberties were taken with the original. *Frankenstein* pleasantly horrified audiences not only in London but in the English provinces, in Scotland, France and America; and in these productions the monster died in a variety of ways, all of them, of course, highly spectacular.

Within our time, Mary Shelley's story has been the theme of at least two stage plays, one of them in Glasgow in 1933, while the various films derived from the subject are too well known to need description here. What a host of weird creatures and events have sprung from that idle conversation held on a rainy summer night so long ago!

Cauld Airn

Ae Februar nicht ane tirled at the pin,
Cryin' wi' fleechin' saftness "lat me in!"
But ootbye, birds were silent, earth was bare,
And I, alane and happit warm in bed,
Daurna sae much as raise my frichted heid
And had nae hert to spier wha tirled there.

Again the voice beseechit "Lat me in!
Look frae the winnock, see, I am your kin:
Tak' doon the horse-shoe frae the lintel heid,
Cauld airn halds me, not this friendly aik.
Be not afeared, I am your faither's maik,
And not a creature frae the ghaistly deid "

And then I minded what my faither cried
The day my mither vanished in a tide
Of weirdly music on the darkling brae,
And hoo he nailed the horse-shoe up at last,
Sayin', in terror, as he held me fast,
"Open to nane the po'er of airn can stay!"

We yirdit him a sennight eftirhaun',
Deid o' his grief and shame, puir, godly man,
Wha feared the sin o' Elfame for his bairn,
But ae nicht, yearning for my fairy mither,
I swear my faither's likeness and nane ither
Cam' ben the hoose and liftit doon the airn!

Haunted theatres

I had not thought of theatres as haunted places until
some years ago when a daily paper alluded to strange
happenings in a Georgian theatre turned bingo hall.
"One more chapter in the long history of theatre
hauntings in Britain" the report added. It was like the
last piece of a jig-saw fitting into place. Of course, what
better setting could there be for the supernatural than
old playhouses where counterfeit loves and passions had
so often clashed with personal tragedy, and a labyrinth
of eerie gas-lit passages lies beyond the stage door.

Delving into the literature of the subject I found
that the theatre in question, the Theatre Royal,
Margate, had a long history of disturbances, and that
the painter who lost his nerve after working alone there
in February, 1966, had simply brought the record more
or less up-to-date.

He complained of uncanny sights and sounds, but
only 11 years before that an assistant manager and
caretaker working there spoke of a series of inexplicable
happenings. These are described in Joseph Braddock's
Haunted Houses, which has an excellent chapter on
theatre ghosts, and included heavy front doors
becoming unbolted in the early hours of the morning,
foyer lights blazing after they had been put out, and an
overwhelming atmosphere of uneasiness.

A recurring feature of the haunting is the
appearance of a tiny ball of light, which passes through
the auditorium getting bigger and bigger as it crosses
the footlights and travels backstage to the stage door. It
is sometimes accompanied by explosive sounds and the
smell of burning or perfume, and has been linked with
the memory of Sarah Thorne, an actress who ran a

drama school there in Victorian times.

But an experienced student of the occult might rather trace the origin of such persistent manifestations to the grim story of the redundant actor in a stock company who committed suicide in full view of the audience. After learning of his dismissal, he engaged a box for the next evening's performance and jumped to his death in the orchestra pit.

Though the tragedy probably dated from the theatre's early days, his ghost appeared in the box as lately as the years before the First World War. So often did this happen that the management were forced to curtain it off, and the space was eventually bricked up. Now it seems that even the intrusion of bingo sessions cannot overlay the powerful atmosphere of the traditional theatre with its vivid emotional life.

Among London's numerous theatre ghosts those of Drury Lane naturally top the bill. W. MacQueen Pope, who chronicled its 300 years of existence in his delightful *History of the Theatre Royal Drury Lane*, not only describes its celebrated daylight ghost, the man in grey, who mingles with the audience, but testifies to having seen him on many occasions. In this he is supported by generations of matinee playgoers and staff, for this revenant from the early eighteenth century is unique in that he only appears between the hours of 9 a.m. and 6 p.m.

He is a handsome man of medium height who wears a powdered wig, three-cornered hat and a grey cloak under which the point of a sword and riding boots are visible. People are inclined to think that he is one of the actors, but no one ever gets close enough to see him properly as he either goes out of focus or materialises at the other side of the upper circle.

The ghosts that linger back-stage and in the dressing-rooms are drawn from the ranks of bygone stars who loved the great playhouse and were proud to appear there. In his book, *Right Hand Left Hand*, Sir Osbert Sitwell tells how the comedian, Stanley Lupino, had reason to believe that this dressing-room was

haunted. Spending a night there, he experienced "vivid
and alarming manifestations".

A second time was when the theatre was brilliantly
lighted, the murmur of the queues outside could be
heard and Lupino was getting ready for the evening
performance. As he applied his make-up before the
mirror he became aware that another face, also in
theatrical make-up, was reflected above his own. It was
smiling, so he winked at it, and the other winked back,
at which he recognised it as the face of his predecessor,
Dan Leno. He could even see a mark across the
forehead where the dead comedian had removed his
wig, and thinking the vision was a trick of some kind,
turned sharply round but there was no one there, and
the door was closed.

Other visible phantoms at "The Lane" have
included a glimpse of Charles II going down the right-
hand gangway with a train of courtiers, but there is
also a benevolent but invisible on-stage presence which
has been known to help nervous or inexperienced
artists, moving them gently into more telling positions
with a touch on the shoulders, followed by a reassuring
pat.

In some theatre hauntings, the ghosts seem to
emanate from the buildings that originally stood on the
site rather than from the playhouse itself. Both Joseph
Braddock in *Haunted Houses*, and E. Thurston
Hopkins in *Ghosts Over England*, describe phantoms
seen in the Old Royalty Theatre in Dean Street that
were obviously attached to the Queen Anne house it
superseded, for some of the old rooms were
incorporated in the theatre fabric. This seems to have
perpetuated the ghost of a woman who appears on the
main staircase, vanishing when she reaches the
vestibule.

Joseph Braddock writes of her as a woman in a
white dress of the Queen Anne period, but in E.
Thurston Hopkin's account she is a gypsy girl in scarlet
and green silk who rattles a tambourine. They have in
common the legend that they were murdered and their

bodies hidden in the recesses of the old house, that of the gypsy being found in a hollow well when the theatre was being built. But she has the distinction of "walking" only when an orchestra is playing, for she was in love with the Romany fiddler who murdered her.

Not surprisingly, the murder of William Terriss in the Adelphi Theatre in 1892 has added to the ghost stories of London's theatreland. This kindly and loved player was the victim of Richard Arthur Prince, a deranged actor, who stabbed him as he was entering the theatre by a private door from Maiden Lane, inflicting a wound from which he died almost immediately.

Since then a good-looking picturesque figure in old-fashioned garb has twice been seen in the vicinity of the tragedy, once in the shadowy alley outside the theatre, and, as recently as January 1956, in Covent Garden underground. Here it was seen by members of the station staff, and subsequently identified as William Terriss after a seance had been held and a photograph of the famous actor compared with a spirit drawing.

Among English provincial theatres an unusual story comes from Christina Hole's *Haunted England*, and relates to the Theatre Royal York, which is believed to be built on the site of an old monastery. In the early hours of the morning, an actress and her sister who were in rooms near the playhouse heard the strains of fine organ music which seemed to come from the theatre. They insisted they were both fully awake at the time, and that they heard it again about an hour later. To this I can add the experience of an aunt by marriage who was on tour there with Sir John Martin Harvey's company. After closing time she found that she had left something in her dressing-room, and went back to the darkened building to fetch it. She was walking along one of the narrow passages when she beheld the figure of a monk walking ahead of her and hastily retreated. Had she perhaps seen the figure of the ghostly organist?

Curiously enough, Scotland, the very home of "ghaisties and ghoulies", has only one theatre haunting on record, and that attaches to a playhouse long demolished, the old Theatre Royal in Shakespeare Square now covered by Edinburgh's General Post Office. It could boast the sounds of a spectral performance, which was often heard by the caretaker and his family who lived above the playhouse.

But surely that is not all. There are historic Scottish playhouses still in existence which are full of dramatic memories. Are we to believe that they are never visited by the shades of past Thespian triumphs?

Strange happenings in the night

Some years ago I started to wonder if our highly technical modern society had left room for the true ghost story, and was intrigued to find a newspaper article headed "Ghost Rush — to Council Houses".

I was still more astonished to learn that churchmen and people with psychic powers were being called upon to exorcise or reason with apparitions, and that a number of housing departments took requests for a change of dwelling with all seriousness.

From then on I cut out every account of ghostly manifestations I could find, a steady trickle of strange happenings which could not be readily explained. Those referred to in "Ghost Rush" had occurred on a council estate near Doncaster, and the local vicar had frequently been roused to deal with them. A haunting at Northfleet in Kent was also described, where the figure of a headless woman terrified council house tenants. In Leeds, a plasterer and his wife suddenly found themselves at the top of the housing list and were offered a terraced house. Their joy was short-lived when they discovered it to be badly disturbed and subject to mysterious footsteps and noises during the night. They learned from neighbours that a man had committed suicide there, and that a child had been killed in a road accident opposite the front gate. Previous tenants had also complained of nocturnal sounds and had kept a small front room locked. A sympathetic housing official had promised to sort things out and a local vicar offered exorcism.

In another case two Army sergeants with spiritualist training managed to convince a revenant that it was no longer alive. Asked why he thought the spectres had deserted great houses for humbler ones, an expert said that they would go wherever people were sensitive enough to pick up the message. Yet recent ghost books suggest that many of them have remained faithful to stately homes, and are calmly accepted there as part of their tradition. There is also a theory that these shadowy folk go on haunting the same piece of ground or air, so that they may have been "inherited" when a council estate was built on the site of a storied mansion.

Even new towns are not immune from such visitations, and in 1969, an eerie case from Livingston in Midlothian affected a young couple with a seven month-old baby. They had to contend with an outbreak of frightening manifestations in which they saw the shape of a white figure sitting in an armchair. Mysterious hand-prints grew visible on walls and windows, round marks appeared on the floor, and once their initials were scrawled above the bedhead. At first they thought someone was playing tricks, but eventually they called in a local priest who blessed their council flat.

Only a few months ago, an Indian family in Kirkcaldy quit a council block where they had lived for two years, and along with other tenants in the block complained of vague supernatural feelings of chill and suffocation. They would not take up residence again, and as no other accommodation could be found for them, they left in haste for Glasgow where friends took them in.

On the other hand, an Alloa housewife confronted with the frequent appearance of a stooped old woman who usually materialised near the fireplace, began to feel pity for her pathetic visitor and came to accept her almost as a friend. Though she and her family were at first appalled by the vision, she had learned that a former occupant of the house had seen her daughter crippled in an accident by fire, and met her own end in flames.

Writers have often used old hostelries as a setting for fictional ghost-stories, but my collection only yields three examples of hauntings in such places. The Kings Arms, Dumfries, boasts a pleasant "guest" in the shape of a charming woman in Victorian dress, who has been there for nearly a century. She is popular with more corporal residents and has taken to sitting in the television room.

But the tragic spectres who scream, the hooded figure who "walks" by night in the twelfth-century inn at Amersham in Buckinghamshire are a different matter. They are said to be the shades of Protestant martyrs held captive before being burned at the stake on the local common, and as a final touch of horror their young daughter was made to light the fire which killed them.

The third example relates to the Palace Hotel in Birkdale, which was scheduled for demolition to make way for a housing estate. When the 11-man crew moved in during spring, 1969, they found it throbbing with supernatural life. Voices were heard in rooms that should have been silent; a lift deprived of electric power kept on working and stopping at the various floors, its gates opened by unseen hands.

Once the sound of a couple arguing was so audible that the workmen hastened to the spot to find nobody there. In the end they found lodgings outwith the site.

Apparently the hotel had a curious history, for it had been built back to front, and the architect had jumped to his death from the top landing.

So persistent is the modern ghostly population of Britain that my cuttings continue to accumulate. Machinery does not seem to baffle them, for a phantom car has been reported from Benbecula, and a driverless bus sighted more than once on the coast road between Prestonpans and Port Seton. Matters are further complicated here by the wraith of an old woman, who drifts across the road after dark and disappears out to sea.

Two of the new Scottish universities have stories of uncanny presences — holidaymakers in a ski-chalet at

Aviemore have recently wakened to see a ghostly Highland warrior glaring at them.

Are these lonely spirits seeking the comfort of human companionship? I would rather hope that they are old sorrows lingering on the atmosphere and, as such, likely to disappear in time.

A curious naming
(related by an old woman who had seen it)

An illegitimate child whose ghost haunted a place in the Lowlands used to lament its lack of a name. One night a drunkard hailed it saying, "Hoos a wi' you short-hoggers", alluding to the footless stockings it wore.

With a cry of joy it vanished.

The seal-woman's son

The seal-women sing on Morven strand,
Alas, that ever I heard their lay,
For I am kin to such as they,
Son of the sea and son of the land.

And in their mournful voices I hear
The lapping of waters, the lure of the deep,
So that my spirit may not sleep
And all my waking is passed in fear.

The earth has my soul, but the water my heart;
My body is riven betwixt the twain,
In mortal travail and ghostly pain,
For flesh and spirit fain would part.

My blood is the sea! This alien land
May never ensnare a child of the wave.
No priest or candle my soul can save,
I seek my mother on Morven strand!

The witch is black affrontit

Aye Gossip — I ken the moon is down,
An' three times three has the hoolet cried —
But I'm no for the coven the night.

I'm no for the Coven,
There's ower muckle shoven,
Wi' huzzies frae Spain,
A' madams frae France,
Set them up wi' their frolics,
'Twad gie ye the colics
To see how they beckon and boo in the dance,
Our dacent Scots Kimmers glower shame at the limmers,
But fi'ent an ane of them fashes a dight.

Their jaunty red heels are kicked up in the reels,
They've invaigled and ogled our spunkiest deils —
So I'm no for the coven the night!

Fife

Magical air of Aberdour

In a lifetime of visits to Aberdour the holiday has always started as the train entered the neat station.

No other place has ever had such a magical effect on me, and I am a little sorry for car-owners made free of Aberdour by the opening of the Forth Road Bridge, who may now never experience the arrival by rail. But surely they will find the spell closing round them as they turn down from the heart of the village to the Shore Road, and reach that part where gardens and houses are terraced high above, and ancient trees frame the first glimpse of blue water.

The road will take them far enough to unload children and picnic gear on the West Beach, that bright crescent of sand which overlooks one of the loveliest views on the Fife coast, with storied Inchcolm lying westward, and Edinburgh's lion hill faintly outlined on the horizon.

At first it is enough joy to relax, but there comes a time when curiosity sets in and the question is whether to go east to the harbour or west to the rocks where the bathers are. My own vote would always go to the harbour beside the old pier, where the coloured boats float lazily beneath a sloping meadow watered by the Dour Burn and the green cliff of the Hawkcraig curves out to sea.

Here the energetic can cut up the hill by the shelters to the woods, and walk through a vast clearing to the Silver Sands. Tradition says that Sir Patrick Spens, of ballad fame, was walking this strand when he received the "braid letter" from the king. On a starlight evening, it has a cool beauty, but alas in the holiday months it is too popular for comfort.

Those who have stayed behind should continue along the leaf-shaded walk which borders the Hawkcraig, where well-placed seats invite sun-bathing. But this is only briefing for an afternoon; visitors of longer duration will find much else to fill the halcyon days, whether they golf, take a boat out, or choose to explore the smiling countryside which cradles Aberdour in green.

If they go westward they will find other ballad memories on the shore near Donibristle, where the Bonnie Earl of Moray met his end on a dramatic night of blood and fire.

To find the roots of Aberdour one must go to the little kirk of St Fillan's, which, like the castle, stands not far from the station. With its crow-stepped gables and beds of growing lavender it seems an endearingly simple country church, but step inside the building and the sturdy Romanesque columns and chancel arch suggest a cathedral in miniature.

Still in its fabric are remains of the early shrine which was under the patronage of the Abbots of Inchcolm, and first received mention in a papal bull of 1178. Of all the architectural changes which have taken place since that distant time, surely the most beneficent has been the careful restoration of 1926, which transformed St Fillan's from a roofless ruin to its present dignified beauty.

Below the west window is the curious Pilgrim Stone, graven with maxims which were probably addressed to those wayfarers who sought the local well of St Fillan. Most were pilgrims suffering from diseases of the eye, and so numerous did they become that a hospice was built for their use in 1475.

This act of mercy was inspired by the vicar of the parish and financed by the first Earl of Morton, whose castle of Aberdour stood near. Other noble families had preceded him there; Viponts, Mortimers, the great Randolph, Earl of Moray, and his own Douglas ancestors. From the fourteenth century or earlier, a massive keep commanded the Dour valley, and through the years it was added to and rebuilt until it was a fine messuage, with gardens and orchards, fishponds, and dovecotes.

Fire, time and tempest combined to ruin the older part, and in 1725, the Earls of Morton, who still own these lands, forsook it for Aberdour House; but the seventeenth-century wing has charm, and the walled garden is a place to linger in.

Aberdour's principal hotel has a reputation for good food which draws visitors from a wide radius, but indeed rooms all over the town are eagerly sought, whether in the few hotels or in the pleasant guest-houses, while houses for the school holidays must be snapped up quickly. For this is the kind of place that is becoming rare, and while the Forth Road Bridge will make it busier than ever before, there will surely remain long periods of utter peace.

This is especially so in spring and autumn, when one wakens to the gentle sighing of trees round the comely old houses, and falls asleep at night to the distant splash of waves on the shore.

St Monance Kirk:
story of an ancient Fife shrine

No photograph quite does justice to the old Kirk of St Monance, so well known to all who love the Fife Coast. The camera shows a comely building with a low steeple that rises from a square tower, the whole edifice looking rather as if it had grown out of the native rock. So far, the impression is true, but perhaps it would require an aerial picture, and certainly a colour film, to capture the full beauty of the ancient church and its environment.

Deep-rooted on a rounded hillock it stands, neighboured by a cluster of old dwellings and overlooking a small bay fretted with curious rocks. In the early spring the scene is full of colour, as the silky blue of sky and sea mingles with the faded pink of tiled roofs and the dim green of mossy walls. These make an unforgettable setting for the massive strength of the ancient shrine which rises high above all, dominating the picture as it has done for nearly 600 years.

After the low, powerful outlines of the exterior of St Monance Kirk, it comes as a surprise to find an interior of lofty delicacy. When I last saw it, it was stripped to the bare walls in preparation for an extensive restoration which took some years to complete. Only a building of the most gracious proportions could have made such an instant appeal to the eye as this fine example of Gothic architecture, lacking all aids of adornment or furnishing.

Presumably intended as a cruciform church, it consists only of a choir and transepts, and does not have the nave, which would have completed the plan. The choir, however, which has four bays, is conceived on spacious lines, soaring upwards to an exquisite vaulted roof. At the intersection of the roof ribbing, which curves in like the branches of a forest glade, are the heraldic shields of great families once linked with the region. Purity of outline and simplicity of carving distinguish the windows of the choir and the canopy of the sedilia on the south wall, and a similar beauty of line is found in the arches which lead to the north and south transepts. It is like looking at the bones of an aged face, too intrinsically handsome to be marred by time.

Legend has been busy with the story of the church's foundation: from the Exchequer Rolls the church is shown to have been raised by Royal edict of King David II, and built between the years 1360 and 1370. The cost, amazingly modest by modern standards, appears to have been in the region of £750, and timber employed during construction was brought from Inverness. Here the facts are fairly definite, but the original reason for building the church is shrouded in a mist of tradition.

The most persistent story, and one which seems nicely appropriate to the site, related how David and his Queen, Margaret Logie, were threatened with shipwreck while crossing the Forth. In their extremity, the King remembered the holy powers of St Monan, a saintly missionary friar whose humble cell had stood on the Fife shore near this spot, and whose virtue still wrought healing miracles to those paying devotions at his shrine. Straightaway, he vowed that if they were brought safely to land, he would raise a great church dedicated to the Saint.

At first, the kirk was evidently not meant for public worship, but simply as a chapel where a friar from the local monastery at Pittenweem would offer up daily prayers in thanksgiving for the Royal succour from drowning. This may account for the modest nature of the original doorway, a small opening on the north wall. Such a status is suggested by the King's deed of gift of the year 1370, conveying certain lands "to God, the Blessed Virgin, and to the chaplains celebrating service in our chapel of St Monans, which we have founded anew". James III bestowed the church on the Black Friars. Later it was annexed to the convent of the West Port of the north gate of St. Andrews. No trace, however, has been found of either monastic or conventual buildings.

That this peaceful shrine has known strife throughout the centuries seems almost incredible, yet not once but several times it has been involved in war. The most recent occasion was in 1941, when it was damaged by the explosion of a German mine washed up on the beach; the first when an English force landed at St Monance in 1544, burned the town, and partly burned the church on their way to the assault on Edinburgh. But when the English came again in 1548, they were repulsed with heavy losses by the youthful Lord James Stuart.

Nor was a marauding band under the half-crazy Earl of Bothwell any more successful towards the end of the sixteenth century, when he descended on St Monance demanding food and quarter, preying also on other Fife towns under the pretext that he was on his way "to take order with the isles".

The sturdy Fifers very properly resisted, and while James Melville, minister of Kilrenny, set off for court to find the King's will in the matter, Bothwell's men were obliged to take refuge in the steeple of St Monance Kirk; otherwise, says Melville pithily, "they had gotten sic wages paid them as had entertained them all their days".

Almost halfway through the seventeenth century, the old shrine entered a new phase as the Parish Church. From this period dates its curious association with the local witches, whose bones after burning were cast in a place in the steeple with the sinister name of "The Burnt Laft". Notable among these unfortunate creatures was one Maggie Morgan, who had taken to the black arts to avenge herself on a faithless lover and those who glossed over his conduct. According to the stories of her spells, she set the whole community by

the ears before she met her dreadful doom on the Kirk
Hill.

Though St Monance Kirk had a congregation which
must have included some wealthy landowners — men
like General Leslie, first Lord Newark, who was
afterwards buried there — it bore the marks of years of
tragic neglect when partial repairs were carried out in
1772. Between then and the 1820's when a major
restoration was effected, the worshippers had only the
use of the choir, which must have looked sadly
overcrowded with galleries on the west, north and east
walls.

But though architecturally regrettable, the galleries
had names which intrigue, particularly the Sailors'
Gallery, which, with the ship model hanging from the
roof of the church served as a reminder of the ancient
calling followed by most of the worshippers drawn from
a fishing community. In such a setting prayers and
hymns from those "who go down to the sea in ships"
had and always will have a special significance, rising to
the great vaulted roof against the ceaseless music of the
waves.

Elie for all seasons

I once spent six months in Elie. It was after a period of
strain, and life in a cottage by the sea seemed an ideal
remedy for frayed nerves. An anxious friend tried hard
to dissuade me from the project, pointing out that a
summer resort would be incredibly dreary out of
season.

Her words came back to me when I got there on an
October day of burning colour. The sea was indigo, the
sky might have been torn from an Italian painting, and
the sands suggested Prospero's island rather than the
East Neuk of Fife. With my back to a sunny wall, I
could have started a tan.

The Royal Burgh of Elie and Earlsferry curls round
Elie Bay like a sleeping cat. Those travelling by train
arrive at the Elie end of the two small towns which
became one in 1929, and as I was bound for the last
loaning in Earlsferry I saw a great deal on that first
journey. I liked what I saw; the comely houses with
shining brass plates and snowy curtains, the glimpses
of old gardens, and the little wynds that branch off the
main road to reach the sea.

I savoured too those hints of Flemish-Dutch
influence which are the East Coast's legacy from bygone
commerce with the Low Countries. They take the eye
pleasantly, with a slant of red pantiled roof, the orderly
scribble of crow-stepped gables, and the toy-box
neatness of steeples like the one on Elie Parish Kirk.

By the time I penetrated the goblin charm of
Earlsferry High Street, where dwellings from more than
one century are good neighbours, I was firmly thirled to
the place.

When I went shopping I usually made a detour by

the South Beach, poking among the wrack cast up by
the tide. Recently I found a sand-encrusted shell in the
pocket of my old tweed coat and remembered the clean-
washed amber strand, the distant view of island and
rock, and the melancholy-sweet piping of sea-birds. I
always ended by climbing the stone ramp to South
Street, where beautiful old houses lean over the water
like the prows of ships, and the imagination is teased by
a carven doorway set into a house of later date.

This once led to the Muckle Yett, the great
mansion of an Elie skipper, one Alexander Gillespie.
Charles II's brother, the Duke of York, had good
hospitality under its roof, sleeping in a bed hung with
apple-green satin, wrought with the Royal Arms of
Scotland.

Farther along the street Elie Castle preserves a
tragic story which wrings the heart with a single lifelike
detail.

It concerns Archbishop Sharp's daughter, who was
living there when she got news of her father's violent
death on Magus Muir. In a passion of grief she set out
to take coach for St Andrews, casting off her high-
heeled shoes to make better speed.

Such tales are almost modern in the burgh's long
story, for the "Ailie of Ardross" was known in Robert
the Bruce's reign, while Earlsferry was ancient when it
figures in a twelfth-century charter of land given by the
Macduffs, Earls of Fife, to the Convent of North
Berwick.

Both towns were created royal burghs in the late
sixteenth century and were fortunate not to lie in the
direct path of history with its wars and tumults. Even
so, the Earl of Mar landed at Elie harbour on his way to
raise the Jacobite standard for the Old Chevalier.

Today Elie's great attraction is golf, with a famous
18-hole course which does credit to the birthplace of
James Braid. It scores, too, with the good kind of
holiday which brings sand into the dining room and
roses to children's cheeks.

Before I left, friends were asking for advice about

hotels, and I sent them the town clerk's leaflet which gave the names of 14 establishments, ranging from a 64-bedroom luxury hotel to the smallest guest-house with four bedrooms.

Acting as a go-between reminded me that my time was nearly over. The winter nights had been magical when the frost sparkled on the red roofs and the wild geese cried overhead. Now I was leaving just as blackbird song filled the gardens. One day I hope to spend the other half of the calendar there. It will be a date worth keeping.

The Passing Pageant

Playing-card curiosities

During the colourful history of the "Devil's Picture Books", as they were so acidly called, many amusing attempts were made by moralists and reformers to turn a popular vice to good account by making it a means of instruction, and from the seventeenth century onwards packs of "freak" playing-cards, published by those with educative, moral, and even political motives, made their appearance.

Among the most curious of these rather futile efforts to reach the masses through their favourite pastime were the *Scholler's Practicall Cards*, published, according to their inventor, "for the recreation of sober and understanding people". With their aid he proposed to inculcate the principles of education in a manner which would remove "the scandall and abuse" into which cards had fallen, but as it was first necessary that the learner should be well versed in at least half a dozen popular card games, the moral value of the plan seems doubtful. In the same class were the *Scientiall Cards*, published in 1651, with a key to their use written "by a lover of ingenuity and learning", which purported to teach the rudiments of "grammar" and which could also be used for an ordinary game.

These were followed by a veritable outpouring of card novelties, and a certain mathematical instrument maker, in a spirit of enterprise considerably ahead of his time, employed the idea as an advertisement, and published a pack of mathematical cards depicting the instruments of his trade and their various uses. Cards were produced for the teaching of geography, history, heraldry, and many other subjects, and were employed

in the youthful education of Louis XIV of France; a
clever notion for arousing childish interest in dull facts.

But the invention of the manufacturers gradually
became exhausted and descended to the ridiculous when
they attempted to enter the realm of domestic affairs
with *The Genteel Housekeeper's Pastime*, published in
1692, which gave instruction in the "correct way to cut
up or carve in the mode all the most usual dishes of
flesh, fish, fowl, and baked meats, with the several
sawces and garnishes proper to each dish of meat."

In this amusing forerunner of Mrs Beeton, the
places of the four suits were taken by different
departments of cookery. The king of spades, who stood
for "baked meats", was depicted with a venison pasty
"rampant". His amiable majesty of hearts came under
the heading "flesh", with a handsome sirloin by his side,
while the kings of diamond and clubs represented
feather and fin in company with a turkey and pickled
herring respectively. Possibly as a variant to scurrilous
broadsheets with "scare" headlines, and with the object
of reaching a wider public, special packs of cards were
printed from time to time by persons with political or
private grievances. These did not mince matters in
announcing their purpose, a pack published in the year
1679 being advertised as: "An History of all the Popish
Plots that have been in England, beginning with those
in Queen Elizabeth's time, and ending with the last
damnable plot against His Majesty Charles II, &c."

A pack of cards which is thought to be the one in
question is conceived in a spirit of characteristic
intolerance; the ace of hearts, for example, showing the
Pope seated at a table with three cardinals and a bishop,
while the devil crouches below. This scene is explained
by the legend, "The Plot first Hatcht at Rome by the
Pope and Cardinalls", and the remaining incidents of the
supposed conspiracy are depicted in an equally lurid
fashion.

Other packs of cards which acted as political and
social commentaries appeared during the succeeding
century, whether animated by a genuine desire for

public enlightenment or merely as sensational novelties it would be hard to say; but there is no mistaking the intention of those published in France during the French Revolution. At such a time even the docile and smirking Royalties encountered on playing cards could not be tolerated for a moment by loyal citizens, so that their places were speedily taken by appropriate figures indicating the trend of public opinion.

A typical example of these productions replaces the four kings by "genii" representing the prevailing ideals of revolutionary France. Thus the king of hearts, incongruously enough, is supplanted by the "Genius of War", armed and surrounded by death-dealing implements; while his consort "Religious Liberty", appears scantily and crudely attired, holding a pile from which flutters a banneret with the words "Dieu Seul". The king of spades has a rather more amiable usurper in the "Genius of Arts", who is the classical Apollo, rather ludicrously adorned with the red cap of Liberty. The kings of diamonds and clubs are ousted by the genii of Commerce and Peace respectively, and the queens of spades, clubs, and diamonds are replaced by three figures representing "Liberty of the Press", "Liberty of Marriage", (a fearsome lady, who flourishes a spike with a streamer bearing the word "Divorce"), and "Liberty of Professions". Even more suggestive of these stirring times are the titles borne by the four knaves, especially the knave of spades — "Equality of Ranks" — who is dressed in the revolutionary style, while the explanatory text on his card alludes to the demolition of the hated Bastille.

Almost equally curious but less ferocious in spirit were those packs which emanated from Republican America. Here vague symbolism was disdained, and practical gratitude to her liberators was shown by replacing the four kings, by four champions of liberty. Thus spades, diamonds, hearts and clubs were ruled over by La Fayette, John Adams (second President of the United States), George Washington, and Benjamin Franklin who, oddly enough, were wedded to Minerva,

Fortune, Venus, and Ceres. The situations left vacant by the banishment of the four knaves were filled by four native American Indian chiefs, the whole making a combination of nationality and temperament which, one feels, would have proved decidedly incompatible in real life.

"The subject is but of smoake"
– tobacco's royal opponent

From his place in the shades, James VI of Scotland must
be chuckling grimly over the present controversy about
tobacco-smoking.

The habit, brought from the American continent,
was scarcely more than 40 years old when the king
became its first distinguished critic in his pamphlet,
A Counterblaste to Tobacco, published anonymously the
year after he mounted the throne of the United
Kingdom.

The tone of his diatribe has a familiar ring, for he
begins more or less by pointing out that his subjects
have never had it so good. "Our peace hath bred
wealth," he writes, "and peace and wealth has brought
forth a general sluggishness which makes us wallow in
all sorts of idle delights and soft delicacies." He goes on
to tell how the tobacco habit came into the country "by
an inconsiderate and childish affection of noveltie,"
borrowed from savages who used it as a preventive or
antidote to a loathsome disease.

At first he is comparatively mild, even a little
indulgently humorous. "Since the subject is but of
smoake, I think the fume of an idle braine may serve
for a sufficient battery against so fumous and feeble an
enemy."

But soon he gets into his true pedagogic swing,
alternating between a kind of paternal lecture and right
royal thundering against this "filthie abuse". It makes
curious reading, yet there is a strong undercurrent of
good sense.

What is most intriguing about the *Counterblaste*,
however, is that it reflects how early social pressures
were brought to bear upon the non-smoker, and how

quick the addict was to claim beneficial results from his solacing pipe. James hunts down such points like a questing terrier.

Most people smoked, he thought, because it was fashionable, or because they "were ashamed to seem singular". Others took it up as "a point of good fellowship . . . he who will not accept is accounted peevish and no good companion".

As for the virtues of tobacco, the smoker of 1604 had not yet thought out the one about ash being good for the floorcovering but he was obviously well advanced on smoking being a grand thing for the health. He believed that it could make him sleepy or alert, and likewise purge the head and stomach of rheume. ("Purged of nothing but what you have bred yourself," retorts James.)

It was even said to help the gout, a notion which really made the king sneer: "In that verie instant when the smoake . . . flies to the head, the vertues thereof . . . . . . run down to the little toe!"

Just how it ensnared and impoverished its victims is also embraced in the royal warnings: "You are not able to walk or ride the journey of a Jew's Sabboth, but you must have a reekie cole brought to you from the next poorhouse to kindle your tobacco with . . . now how you are by this custome disabled in your goods, let the Gentry of the Lande bear witness, some of them bestowing three, some four hundred pounds a yeare upon this precious stinke."

Nor does he forget to have a swipe at the trooper who nipped behind a byre wall to have an illicit puff; he was sure that smoking militated against fitness for war, and sternly admonished, "If anie of you should seek leisure to stay behind his fellows for taking of tobacco — I should never be sorie for anie evil chance that might befall him."

As for smoking at table, it had evidently begun even then, and the mere remembrance of it rouses King James to heights of denunciation, as he says what he feels — and what many people have felt since — about the uncleanliness of those who blow "filthie smoake and stinke . . . athwart the dishes".

But if the pattern of smoking was fixed early, the pattern of taxing it was not long in following, led by the monarch who clapped a heavy impost on tobacco not long after the publication of his pamphlet.

His reasons were ostensibly fatherly, and directed at combating a dangerous habit, but the picture of benevolence is rather spoiled by the fact that he proceeded to grant small monopolies and concessions in the trade — at fat fees.

Charles I continued to show righteousness by justifying the giving of monopolies, advancing as one of his reasons that it was to curb the excessive use of tobacco north of the Border. Tax-gatherers who followed hardly bothered excusing themselves for tapping a source so productive and easily controlled. During the turbulent seventeenth century, with its confusion of religious wars, the smoker was "milked" again and again. First it was the Covenanting Parliament, which promised the new impost would only endure, "so long as the necessities of the armie should require it, at the farthest but for ane year," then had to come back for more.

Later the Scot in the Capital had to plank down more to fill his clay pipe, because funds were needed to pay for the building and repairing work going on in Auld Reekie.

So from the first century of its existence in this country the story of tobacco has a curiously familiar sound. There is even James VI's assertion that it was bad for the lungs, and his sinister description of a heavy smoker's likely internal condition to bring it quite up to date. Writing in 1604 he declared that such a man's inward parts would be "soiled and infected with an unctious and oily Soote", and who is to say that he was very far wrong?

Romantic tale of the Heart of Montrose

A mummified heart, believed to be that of the first Marquis of Montrose, is being sent to Scotland. It is in the possession of Mrs Maisie Hurley of Vancouver, a descendant of the Great Marquis, who is bequeathing it to a cousin, Mr Christopher Campbell Johnston.

The adventures of Montrose's heart, as recorded in the writings of the Napier and Johnston families, showed it to be one of the most travelled relics in Scottish history up to the time of the French Revolution, when it disappeared completely.

When the Marquis of Montrose was betrayed and executed in 1650, after leading the Royalist forces in Scotland, his body was dismembered and buried in a nameless grave in the Boroughmuir. Through the efforts of Lady Napier, wife of the Marquis' nephew, his precious heart was taken from his body, and after being embalmed by an Edinburgh surgeon was put into an egg-shaped steel case, made from Montrose's sword blade. This in turn was placed in a gold filigree box of Venetian workmanship, which had belonged to the famous mathematician, Napier of Merchiston, and was kept in a silver urn.

A deep affection had existed between Montrose and the young Napiers, and he had promised to bequeath his heart to Lady Napier as a mark of regard for her kindness. Now that the relic had so tragically come into their care, she showed her reverence for the great man's memory by having her portrait painted with the silver urn, and by keeping it on a table by her bed. After a time she seems to have felt that the heart should have been in his son's possession, and sent it to the young marquis, then in exile with Lord Napier in Holland.

Now came the first of its astonishing disappearances and recoveries, for the relic went missing, and was only found by chance through a friend of Lord Napier's, who identified it in the collection of an antiquary in Holland. By this time the silver urn had vanished, but the heart and its steel case were still intact inside the gold box.

It was handed back to the Napier family, and in time inherited by Hester — afterwards Hester Johnston — great-great-granddaughter of the Lady Napier who had first procured it. This young girl had been thrilled by its romantic story as a child, and when, some years later, she went to India with her husband and small son, she carried the relic in a velvet reticule, along with other family treasures. On the voyage their ship was attacked by a French frigate, and an enemy shot which wounded her and the child also shattered the gold filigree box.

Miraculously, the inner steel case and the heart were intact, and an Indian goldsmith was found who not only reproduced the gold box, but made a replica of the missing silver urn, working from descriptions. On the latter, an account of Montrose's life and death was engraved, translated into Tamil and Telugoo, the two languages then most commonly understood in the Southern Peninsula of India.

· The relic was kept in the Johnston's house at Madura, and because it was regarded by the natives as a talisman, was stolen and sold to a chief of some importance. This chief, who was a man of outstanding character, happened to be the host of Hester's son, and was much impressed by the brave fashion in which the boy beat off and wounded a wild boar which attacked his horse while they were hunting.

He asked him what he would like as a mark of the occasion, whereupon Alexander begged that the heart of Montrose should be restored to his family. The chief, who had not known that it was stolen originally, immediately returned it, and, loading the boy with gifts for himself and his mother, sent a letter to her, expressing his regret that she had suffered so much distress over its loss.

The last chapter of its early history came when the Johnstons left India, and, finding themselves in France during the Revolution, put the urn with its contents temporarily into the keeping of an Englishwoman called Knowles to avoid its confiscation by the French Government. Unfortunately Miss, or Mrs Knowles, who lived in Boulogne, died before the urn could be conveyed across the Channel, and the precious relic was lost once again. This was, however, perhaps not quite the end of the story, for in a series of First World War memoirs published in a Scottish magazine during the 'thirties, a Scottish soldier was mentioned as having run a gaming table during his leave in France. One night a French poilu laid down as surety for his stake a curiously shaped steel box, reclaiming it later when he won. When describing the incident later to the author of the memoirs, the amateur croupier speculated idly as to the contents of the box.

His better-informed friend was certain that he had let a treasure pass from his keeping. "You fool!" he exclaimed; "that was the heart of Montrose."

Probably no one will ever know if this was so, but it would be fascinating to trace the rest of the story in all its details. Surely it is one of the most romantic tales ever found in a byway of history, doubly appealing because it attached to the memory of such a noble man.

Arthur's seat, and Arthurian localities in Scotland

The name of the great lion-shaped hill which looms over the Palace of Holyroodhouse and its gardens, has been variously translated as "Hill of the Arrows" and "Ard-na-Sidhe" ("Hill of the Fairies").

I am inclined to favour the latter, after hearing the story that an old serving-man who worked in the beautiful little Regency house (Arthur Lodge) that lay beside it, told a departing guest that "Arthur and the Auld Picts" were supposed to sleep within its interior.

Other Arthurian localities include "Merlin's Grave", near the River Tweed, while Camelon (Falkirk) has been equated with Camelot. Interesting, too, is the existence of Merlindale in Peebleshire. This suggests a definite link between Arthurian legend and that part of Scotland.

The pipes of Lucknow

Most great events have their accompanying legends; dramatic tales of human interest which often outlive historic truth in popular imagination. It is safe to say that people who have only the vaguest mental picture of the Indian Mutiny knows the story of the Pipes of Lucknow, which tells how a Highland girl in the beleaguered garrison heard in a dream the bagpipes of the relieving force.

It is over a hundred years since Victorian Britain was stirred to its depths by news of the Relief of Lucknow, the first part of which was achieved by Sir Henry Havelock and the 78th Highlanders. His force had in turn to be liberated from the besieged town by another body of troops under Sir Colin Campbell, but its arrival on the 25th of September, 1857, was the turning point, and staved off certain death for the exhausted garrison.

That night, a Mrs Inglis, who kept a full diary of the siege begun in July, records that she was kept awake by the noise of the celebrations among the friendly Sikhs in the garrison, and mentions also that Mr Rees, a Calcutta merchant in the Residency, did not go to bed until 3 a.m. after dancing to the pipes of the Highlanders. But she says nothing of the dream about the pipe music which was to become the legend of Lucknow.

In this country the story was first printed in *The Times* of December 14th, 1857. It was contained in a letter from M. de Banneroi, French physician to Mussur Rajah, which had appeared in the Parisian paper *Le Pays*, under the date *Calcutta, October 8*. The episode had been described to M. Banneroi by a lady who was one of the rescued garrison, and was set forth at some length. Those in Lucknow knew that they could hold out for only another twenty-four hours, and had resolved to die rather than give in. The women were trying to encourage each other, and to continue their light duties of carrying orders and refreshments to the men at the batteries. The lady who told the story had gone out on one of these errands, accompanied by Jessie Brown, the wife of a corporal in her husband's regiment. The Highland girl had been in a state of restless excitement "all through the siege" (in itself a remarkable condition to sustain for a period of over two and a half months). She had not been well for some days, and her mind wandered, returning to thoughts of home.

Worn out, she wrapped herself in her plaid and lay down on the ground, asking her companion to wake her when "her father should return from the ploughing". The narrator herself was soon asleep with Jessie's head in her lap, but was presently awakened by a "wild unearthly scream" close to her ear. She saw Jessie standing upright with raised arms, her head bent as if listening, then a look of delight came into her face and she exclaimed: "Dinna ye hear it? Dinna ye hear it? Ay, I'm no dreamin', it's the slogan o' the Highlanders, we're saved, we're saved!"

The remainder of the tale, told with suspiciously dramatic aplomb, goes on to relate how Jessie ran to the men at the batteries crying: "Courage, courage, hark to the slogan — to the MacGregors, the grandest o' them a'. Here's help at last." For a moment, we are told, they stopped firing and listened anxiously. Then came a murmur of disappointment, and as the Colonel shook his head, the wailing of the women who had crowded round broke out afresh. Jessie, however, lay on the ground once more, then sprang to her feet again, crying in a voice so piercing that it was heard along the whole line: "Will ye no' believe it noo? The slogan has ceased, indeed, but the Campbells are comin'. D'ye hear, d'ye hear?"

"At that moment," says the narrator, "we seemed

indeed to hear the voice of God in the distance, when
the pibroch of the Highlanders brought us tidings of
deliverance, for now there was no longer any doubt of
the fact. That shrill, penetrating, ceaseless sound which
rose above all other sounds, could come neither from
the advance of the enemy nor from the work of the
Sappers. No, it was indeed the blast of the Scottish
bagpipes, now shrill, now harsh, as threatening
vengeance to the foe, then in softer tones seeming to
promise succour to their friends in need."

According to the rest of the story, the members of
the garrison knelt in prayer, then they gave a shout of
joy. To their cheers and cries of "God Save the Queen"
the pipers replied with the strains of *Auld Lang Syne*.
The story-teller ends by saying "I scarcely remember
what followed", an odd remark for one who had
remembered so much, but she does recall that Jessie
was presented to the General as he entered the fort,
and that her health was drunk that night by all
present, while the pipers marched round the table, once
more playing *Auld Lang Syne*.

A critical Scot could have immediately picked holes
in such a story, which soon found its way into one of
the principal illustrated magazines; but at a time of
national thanksgiving the mood is hardly analytical. It
fell to a sharp-eyed correspondent of *Notes and Queries*,
writing in the following February, to point out some
distinct flaws in the narrative. He wanted to know
whether Jessie's "intensely acute ear" had caught the
war-cry of the MacGregors, "or whether the writer had
been referring to the pibroch, perhaps, 'The
MacGregor's Gathering'." He goes on to say that he
was unaware that ancient slogans were in use among
any Highland troops, and that he thinks the narrator
had confused slogan with pibroch.

By May 1858 the same writer is even more critical,
and reports a devastating paragraph from the Calcutta
correspondent of *The Nonconformist*: "We have read
with some surprise and amusement that wonderful
story published in the English papers about Jessie

Brown and the slogan of the Highlanders in Havelock's Relief of Lucknow, and I have been assured by one of the garrison that it is pure invention: 1. No letter of the date mentioned could have reached Calcutta when the story is said to have arrived. 2. There was no Jessie Brown in Lucknow. 3. The 78th neither played their pipes nor howled out the slogan as they came in. They had something else to do. 4. They never marched round the dinner table with their pipes the same evening at all."

Commenting on this information the correspondent adds that the story bears the marks of fiction, and observes irritably that one of the most curious things connected with it was the appearance of songs and ballads by Scots writers who adopted the confusion of slogan and pibroch. Strangely enough, no one wrote to tell him that he was confusing a type of pipe music with the pipes themselves in his use of the word pibroch!

But though the story had been quickly denied, a subject so apt for dramatic and literary exploitation was not to be easily dropped. Dion Boucicault wrote a three-act play on the theme which was produced for Wallack's Theatre, New York, where it ran for over 80 nights, while the piece was given in England at the Theatre Royal in Plymouth.

Then at least four sets of verses were composed with Jessie as heroine, one of them by an American, R. T. S. Lowell, but the best-known was that by a Scottish versifier, Grace Campbell, which was set to music in the early sixties by John Blockley, and was still current when the author was at school in 1914. Entitled "Jessie's Dream at Lucknow", it began:

"Far awa' to Bonnie Scotland
Has my spirit ta'en its flight,
And I saw my mither spinnin'
In oor Hieland hame at night."

The firm hold it had taken on the popular imagination is shown by the fact that as late as 1910, a picture dealing with the romantic story of Jessie's experience was published in the Christmas number of the *London Magazine*, while in October 1911, a correspondent to *Notes and Queries* was still aluding to the tale as if it had been founded on fact.

What was probably the root of the matter was dug up, and not for the first time, in November 1911, when a correspondent in *Notes and Queries* refers to the statement of a certain Mr Crowest, writing in the *National Review* in 1889, on the music of the British Army. Of the Lucknow story Mr Crowest says:- "This Highland lassie never lived in the flesh, it was the imaginative creation of a lady who had cultivated her ruling faculty by much writing for the newspapers and magazines. The lady thought that a Highland lassie in the beleaguered city would be good copy. The Highland Lassie of Lucknow in fact made the tour of the world in print, and though there was absolutely not one word of truth in the whole story, she probably will not receive her official and final contradiction until the Judgement Day."

Countless stories of true heroism and endurance were eventually told of the brave men and women besieged in Lucknow, which makes it all the stranger that a deliberate invention should receive such prominence. Perhaps in its picturesque detail it served both as a focal point for the nation's applause of this communal gallantry, and a tribute to the Scottish soldiers who relieved the city.

Immortal Harlequin

It wanted a few minutes to midnight and twenty-four hours to the Hogmanay that would usher in the year 1880. A wind like a wolf roamed the bridge which links Auld Reekie with the New Town of Edinburgh, and the policeman on the beat halted reluctantly to shine his lamp into the shadows of the General Post Office, where all the gas-lights but one had fallen prey to the storm.

The inspection was as perfunctory as he dared make it, for he had no wish to turn some poor, derelict creature out into the icy blast. Tomorrow his problem would be Hogmanay revellers, well-warmed with drink and probably singing. Tonight only those without hearth or home were abroad.

As his eyes grew accustomed to the fitful light within the great entrance hall, he made out the shape of a man asleep, head pillowed on a shabby carpet bag, and long great-coat drawn closely round him. Outside the wind gave a questing howl, and the sleeper turned to reveal a face old and incredibly fine-drawn. Not for the first time in his life, the constable regretted his calling. "Ye canna stay here, sir," he said, but mildly enough. "Have ye nae place to go?"

The ancient sat up, his lips moved, and it was like a ghost speaking. "I was tired," he mumbled. "I am just out of hospital this morning and went down Leith Street to my old lodging. But in my absence my landlady had died. I have been walking about all day."

The policeman straightened himself and nodded. At this season the city was full of such miseries. "You could try the Night Asylum," he suggested. "At least you would have a roof over your head." "I had rather

not," said the old man with some dignity, "if you give me another ten minutes to get my strength back, I have a friend who might put me up."

It was a noble lie and they both knew it, but the policeman turned and went on his way. If he could not help the poor body, at least he could let him keep his self-respect.

Left to himself the old man tried to rise, but his legs refused their task. Limp as a discarded coat, he sank to the ground just as a tall youth strode into the hall, whistling gaily. Before he could cry out, the stranger had almost fallen over him on his way to the posting-box.

Regaining his balance, the newcomer was explosive. "Gracious heavens! What are you doing there?" "Dying, I believe," said the old man apologetically. Fumbling in his pocket, the other struck a match. It briefly illumined his thin good-humoured face, and clothes of Bohemian cut. "You can't die here!" he remonstrated, shivering as the wind made a fresh sally into the hall. The figure on the ground drew a quick, harsh breath. "There are worse places to take a last curtain," he whispered, "and this one has memories for me." The youth was incredulous. "Memories? This great stone barn?" "I was not thinking of this upstart building," said the old man, with the contempt of age for anything less than a century old. "I refer to the elegant Theatre Royal of Shakespeare Square that once stood here. . . ." He was halted by a violent fit of coughing, and the young man ran outside with the confused idea of seeking help. With relief he hailed the burly figure of the policeman, now on his homeward beat. "There's a sick man here," he said urgently. "I think he may be dying. Can you get him to hospital?" "Ay, is he still there?" said the other. "I thocht he was gey far through, but he wad hae it that he had a freend wad tak' him in. Wad ye bide wi' him, sir, till I fetch a conveyance?" The young man nodded, and went back to the still figure on the ground.

"I have a flask," he said. "A mouthful of brandy will put new life into you." He raised the slender body, insubstantial as an armful of withered leaves, and the old man took a sip. "I see you are ready for the Daft Days," he said with faint humour. "It is sixty years since I was here at this season. I played Harlequin, and Violetta was my Columbine." He fell silent for a time, struggling for breath, then a whisper came. "Happy . . . we were so happy until. . . ." "Hush!" said the young man gently. "You weary yourself. Lie quiet until help comes."

Once more the old man tried to sit up but failed. "Quiet!" he expostulated, "I can throw my voice the whole length of this theatre! Stand back . . . at the very back of the pit if you like and you will hear me. . . ." He gestured weakly, but with histrionic passion.

The other retreated until he stood outside, beyond one of the lofty arches. He could see the handsome old face, see the lips moving, but no sound came, and at length all was still.

Tears filled his eyes, and in the moonlight made a rainbow nimbus within which the sparkling figures of Columbine and Clown emerged from the shadows. One on either side they bent over the old man and raised up immortal Harlequin. Young, radiant, joyous, the three linked arms, gave a restful leap, and melted into the darkness.

The rumble of wheels on the frosty road announced the return of the policeman, more than half ready for the news awaiting him.

"I jalouse he's awa'?" he asked.

"He is Harlequin again," said the young man gladly, slipping his handkerchief into his pocket.

Verses

The saving of Stonehenge

Here in this ring our island's ancient faith
Burned like a secret flame, when England lay
Crushed by the Roman sandal. Free from scathe,
The older gods of Britain stood at bay,
And knew themselves immortal. For they were
Flesh of the soil and vocal in the wind,
Invincible to every conqueror
Seeking their refuge in the native mind.

And now, till time is ended, they are made
Franklins of the rare zone which girds them round,
Walking in peace within their stony glade,
Shades of an older world on friendly ground.

February's music

Rain songs for April in slender silver notes,
Caught and returned by feathered throats,
Green slippers for her dancing feet,
Laughter in every wind, that floats —
And all the waking world to call her sweet.

Violets and cowslips for March's dower,
Diamond be-spangled in a shower.
The trumpeters of earth and sky,
Shrilling beneath the casements of her bower,
Salute her with triumphant harmonies.

But only quiet February can wear,
The dead-white snowdrop in her hair,
Anemones in her gown;
And have for music in the icy air
A lone linnet's song to the four winds blown.

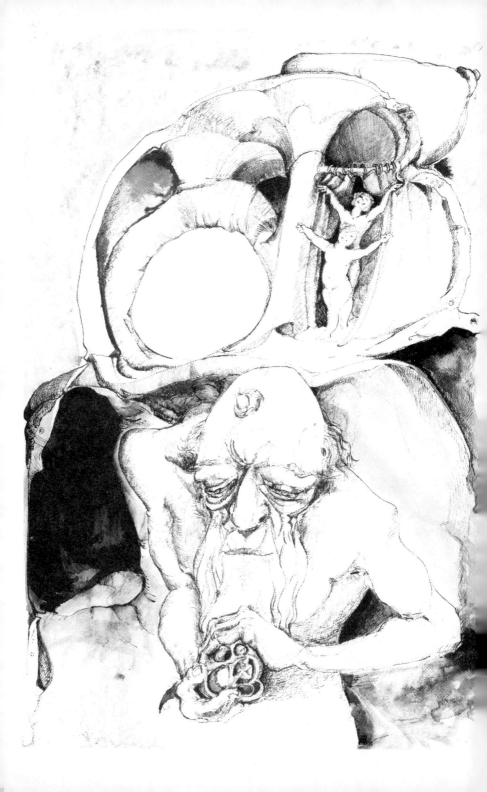

The Auld Year

Oh, see the Auld Year gang his gate,
A runkled carle wi' a snowy pate,
Girnin' early an' grummlin' late,
Draigelt, cross and cankered.

He's laith to hear oor last "Guid nicht!"
And kens we want him frae oor sicht,
To greet the New Year trig and ticht,
And toast him in a tankard.

But yet the Auld was aince my jo,
My hert is wae to see him go,
Dune wi' daurg and hirplin slow,
When aince for him I hankered!

The tinkler poet

I'll tak' my way when day is dune,
An' all I ask is ae star's licht;
I'll no' ha'e the peerin' mune
To blin' me wi' her lantern bricht.

Ilk waygaun shadow is a frien',
There's nocht to fear aneath the sky,
The dark to me is wife and wean —
I want nae licht to lose them by.

But juist ae dancin' star ayont,
Adventure ca'in on the wind,
The cauldrife day alane can daunt
A tinkler wi' a poet's mind.

The drowned cathedral

Here at the river's edge are seen
Shadows of spires and hints of olden stone,
The shapes of carven flowers
The grace of spectral towers
Drowned and held captive in a green
And pagan cavern of waters lone.

The solemn chimes which sang of prayer
Writhe in a shrill and wanton elfin measure,
Filling the ruined halls,
From door to choir-stalls
With music fashioned for unearthly pleasure
And clamorous voices of the sea and air.

Dream waters

Green lakes and silent waters are
Cool windows in this fiery star,
    Through which, when pent without escape,
We gaze in sleep and float afar
    Round some imaginary cape.

Trailing hot fingers through the clair
And icy waters of the air,
    Sailing a boat of emerald glass
Near dreaming island shadows where
    Old temples glimmer as we pass

Hearing a music from the strings
Of some white siren as she sings
    Divinely to a silver lute —
But darkness folds her friendly wings,
    And dawning makes the singer mute!

The blossom tree

O bury me where blossoms blow,
But let me hear the city's voice,
For I would lie where people go
Each year to see the trees rejoice.
There is a church-yard in the town
Where cherry-blossom wears its dress,
And filmy petals flutter down,
Veiling the dead in loveliness.
For that is all that Death can be —
Frail blossoms fall at last to earth,
But every year the silver tree renews the miracle of birth.

Enchanted bird

As I lay on the hill in Autumn weather,
A ballant cam' doon like a bird to the hand.
Glamourie shone frae ilka feather,
And its een were winnocks on an unkent land.

It sang "My heart is a siller mune,
And in its planet a crystal sphere,
And in the sphere a harper's tune
Is key to all the warldis lear.

But gin ye rieve yon mune for treasure,
The crystal sphere will fa' in twain,
And so be tyned all music's pleasure,
For whilk the saul of man is fain.

O wha will tether my rainbow pinions,
O wha will fashion my cage o' goud?
He that has wandered the sky's dominions,
He that has trodden the shores o' cloud!"

The forsaken fountain

Here once there played a fountain,
Tossing its crystal feathers in the air;
Coming from hanging woods
And far-off mountain,
Cooling the aureate hours
Of the bright south.
O happy water!
Ocean young in sport,
Come not too late to wake
The dying rose
In the dry fountain's smoothly hollowed bed;
But with your harping
And your laughter
As would revive both rose and quiet rill,
Make music in this
Silent court.

Queen's tragedy

Yule was held at Holyrude House
With wine and sang and meikle laughter,
With never a thocht for what cam' after;
The clash of words,
The sorrow of swords.
Queen Mary pledged her yellow-haired spouse,
Fair and fain in a cramoisie gown.
She dropped a pearl in his wine for token
Of luve and longing yet unspoken.
But pearls are tears, and the waefu' years
Set mony a pearl in the Scottis croon:
And luve and luver and pearl were dust
Ere mony munes had waxed and withered,
And Scotland's fairest Queen had gathered
The thorny flowers of saikless hours
When wine was ashes and song was rust.

The Dream Castle

The Dream Castle

I dreamed last night that I had been left a small castle
by someone who wanted to remain anonymous. "That
astonishes me," I said, "where is it and has it got a
ghost?"

"The choice is yours," he said, "and yes, the one we
had in mind lives in a well in the court-yard. A castle
without a ghost is no use. She wears a green dress
covered with silver spangles, and after climbing out of
the well peeps through your bedroom window as the
church clock strikes twelve."

"Isn't that a bit shivery?" I demurred, "I don't think
I'd like that."

"You're supposed to shiver," he said.

Remember we're in the Daft Days and what they
call the Celtic fringe — Scotland, Ireland and Wales,
have always contributed liberally when it comes to
doing something really queer.

"Whoop-ee," I said, drawing on my brightest
dressing-gown. "I want to dance but I've no partner."

"You've got as far as 1989," he said. "Would you
prefer me to ask some attractive gentleman ghost to
give you a hand?"